GEM TRAILS
OF
PENNSYLVANIA AND
NEW JERSEY

By
Scott Stepanski
and
Karenne Snow

Gem Guides Book Co.
315 CLOVERLEAF DRIVE, SUITE F
BALDWIN PARK, CA 91706

Library of Congress Catalog Card Number 99-76138
ISBN 1-889786-09-8

Maps: Scott Stepanski and Dusty Stepanski
Cover: Paul Morrison

NOTE:
    Due to the possibility of personal error, typographical error, misinterpretation of information, and the many changes due to man or nature, *Gem Trails of Pennsylvania and New Jersey*, its publisher and all other persons directly or indirectly associated with this publication assume no responsibility for accidents, injury or any losses by individuals or groups using this publication.
    In rough terrain and hazardous areas all persons are advised to be aware of possible changes due to man or nature that occur along the gem trails.

TABLE OF CONTENTS

PENNSYLVANIA

NEW JERSEY

Map Symbols

Interstate Highway

U.S. Highway

(23) (143) State Highway (PA/NJ)

T380 Township Road (PA)

S. R. 1006 State Road (PA)

135 Forest Road (PA)

626 Spur 563 County Route (NJ)

34 Interchange

Town or Park

Buildings

Specific Building

Parking Lot

Quarry, Road Cut or Borrow Pit

North

Mine

X Collecting Site

Small Bridges

Large Bridge

Pullover or Parking Area

Railroad

OVERVIEW MAP

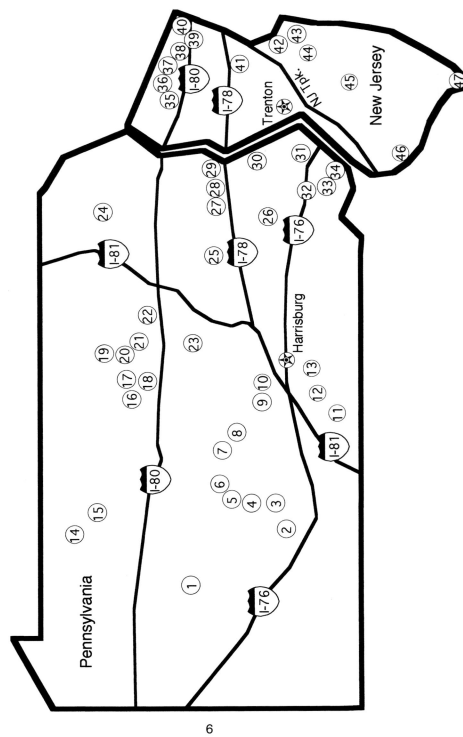

KEY TO SITES ON MAP

PENNSYLVANIA

SITE NO.

1. Shelocta Siderite Concretions
2. New Paris Fluorite
3. New Enterprise Banded Chert
4. Roaring Spring Quartz & Chert
5. Grazierville Shale Concretions
6. California Quarries
7. Huntingdon Fossils
8. Mapleton Galena
9. Ickesburg Trilobites
10. New Bloomfield Devonian Fossils
11. Mt. Hope White Quartzite
12. Mt. Holly Springs Agate
13. Rossville Copper Minerals
14. Kinzua Dam Fossils
15. Highland Picture Sandstone
16. Lock Haven Ripple Marks
17. Jersey Shore Calcite & Quartz
18. Antes Creek Fossils
19. Ralston Fossil Leaves
20. Williamsport Ammonites
21. Crystal Point Diamond Mine
22. Montour Fossil Pit
23. Eastern Industries Quarry
24. Carbondale Fossil Ferns
25. Deer Lake Brachiopods
26. Morgantown Minerals
27. Vera Cruz Jasper
28. Hellertown Jasper & Quartz
29. Eastonite
30. Ringing Rocks Park
31. Wissahickon Valley Garnets
32. Phoenixville Dolomite
33. Chrome Run Minerals
34. Prospect Park Kyanite

NEW JERSEY

SITE NO.

35. Lime Crest Quarry
36. Sterling Hill Mine
37. Buckwheat Dump
38. Lake Valhalla Yellow Serpentine
39. Basalt Quarry Minerals
40. Schuyler Copper Mine Dumps
41. Stirling Brook Carnelian
42. Cliffwood Beach
43. Poricy Park Fossil Beds
44. Big Brook Fossil Shark Teeth
45. Pine Barrens Bog Iron
46. Salem Jasper Gravel
47. Cape May Diamonds

SPECIAL THANKS TO:

Vallery Barnwell, Jon D. Beam, Dave Boston, Richard Bostwick, Jim Brouse, Warren Cummings, Louise Darby, Christine Dodge, Eastern Industries, Inc., Franklin Mineral Museum, Franklin-Ogdensburg Mineralogical Society, William Gallagher, Jon Gladwell, Ned Gilmore, Joseph P. Gurekovich, Richard Haefner, David Harper, Bob Hauck, Allan W. Holman, Jr., Linda M. Houston, Ginette Isenberg, Chet Lemanski, Limestone Products Corporation, Albert Mabus, Terri Martinsen, Judy Maston, Alfred Mayerski, Steve Misiur, Montclair State University, Montour Preserve, Leonard Morgan, MJ & Jack Murphy, New Enterprise Stone & Lime Co., Maxine Nino, Robin Nordhues, William L. Patton, Philadelphia Mineralogical Society, Poricy Park Nature Center, Robin Prim, Charles J. Randall, Beverly Rozewicz, Steve Sanford, John D. Scott, William Sherpinsky, Ray Smith, Robert Smith, Robert C. Smith, Birch Snider, Bob Stager, Dusty Stepanski, Walter Stepanski, Sterling Hill Mine & Museum, Strawberry Hill Nature Center & Preserve, Phil & Allison Stoner, Ralph Thomas, Dennis Thomasik, Lee Tori, John H. Way, Gary Weinstein, Wilfred Welsh, Ralph Wentz, Bear Wertz, Ed Wilks, Tracie L. Witter.

PREFACE

"There's nothing left to collect...."

That is an old mineral collecting lament that we hear far too often in Pennsylvania and New Jersey. True, the region's heyday of miners and mineral-rich deposits is long past. The history of mining and the more personal story of the miners themselves are often only evidenced by overgrown and barely remembered mine spoils. The places speak quietly to a few who pause and listen, of the human struggle that brought the minerals to the surface.

The old works, sadly, do not usually speak loudly enough. Many are gone and still more will follow in the wake of modern development. We visited many former collecting sites turned golf course, apartment complex or shopping mall in the course of our research. Such visits can naturally lead to the feeling that there is nothing to collect. We, however, consistently returned from other trips with samples of beautiful agate, jasper, galena, pyrite, quartz crystals and much more.

There is something to collect in Pennsylvania and New Jersey! Sometimes you need to brush away the fallen leaves or walk a little farther, but it is there all the same. Best of all, new collecting locations do open up from time to time. We hope that this book will help both new collectors and old to view the landscape with a fresh eye and enthusiasm. Veteran collectors may recognize some collecting sites and be surprised at the absence of others. We chose the locations for their variety and availability. A few outstanding quarry sites included here are open only on certain days or conditions, and they are certainly worth the wait. We chose most of the sites, however, for their access to collectors on any occasion.

Collecting sites in *Gem Trails of Pennsylvania and New Jersey* are a culmination of field trips, library research, interviews with collectors and serendipity. The final category is the one we find most exciting and which put the final polish on our travels. We stopped and looked as often as we could whether it was a road cut, stream erosion or someone digging a ditch. While we invite you to explore the locations in the book we also invite you to explore beyond the book and discover even more collecting locations.

Just stop and look.

Scott Stepanski
Karenne Snow

INTRODUCTION

PENNSYLVANIA AND NEW JERSEY: AN OVERVIEW

The land continually reminds us of the world's ever changing natural environment. From Pennsylvania's western plateau to the coastal plain province of southern New Jersey rests a landscape marked by time. Between plateau and plain is a twisted and deformed region of scarps, valleys, and sediment and metamorphic ridges that formed during repeated collisions with other land masses. The long history of our wandering continent slowly emerges from beneath the quiet countryside and urban terrain. An artistry of change inscribes the land and continues to shape our world today. Gems, minerals and fossils gathered by collectors are mementos of that change.

In human terms, the effect of geology in everyday life is both subtle and grand. Interstate highways and road networks blaze across the states, over streams and through the hearts of Appalachian mountains. Passengers on such busy arteries are often scarcely aware of the rock layers and sediment exposed here and there by road cuts, stream banks and endless weathering. Even so, as the passengers mark their progress, they are turned, routed and deflected by the winding course of rivers, deformed mountains and eroded valleys. Truckers, travelers and rock collectors are all ultimately led by the geology of the land.

The Appalachian Plateau Province, combining the Allegheny and Pittsburgh Plateaus to the north and west, and Pocono Plateau in the northeast, dominates more than three-quarters of Pennsylvania. The Plateau Province covers all of Pennsylvania west of Bedford and Blair County, except for a band of lowland on the shores of Lake Erie. The plateau then hooks northwest through Wyoming County and down into Carbon County. The eastern edge of the province is marked by a prominent scarp called the Allegheny Front.

The plateau surface is not flattened like a typical plateau. Small mountains cover the area carved by stream erosion of the sedimentary layers. In addition, the movement of ice age glaciers scarred and altered from the northwest and the northeast corners of the plateau. The last period of glaciation, called the Wisconsin, ended roughly 10,000 years ago. The effect of the Late Wisconsin glaciation is the most visible in Pennsylvania and New Jersey because of its recent vintage.

Sedimentary layers of the plateau are gently folded deposits from the Silurian period 440 million years ago to the Permian period ending about 225 million years ago. Ancient seas covered and receded from the plateau area periodically before its uplift. These ancient seas deposited layers of fossils in the sediment. Devonian marine fossils at Kinzua Dam and nearby terrestrial plant fossils in sandstone mark changes in the Pennsylvania environment over time. Sedimentary deposits in the plateau frequently contain nodules of siderite such as those in the exposed Pennsylvanian Age deposits near Shelocta.

East and south of the plateau is the Valley and Ridge Province that reaches through Pennsylvania at Bedford County and bends upward into northern New Jersey. The Valley and Ridge Province continues along the East Coast the entire length of the Appalachian chain. As the name suggests, the Valley and Ridge section is a continuous belt of ridges and valleys. New Jersey's highest elevations of about 1,800 feet are within the Valley and Ridge. Beneath the province are folded sequences of sedimentary rocks.

The final convergence of the African and North American Tectonic Plates that formed the Valley and Ridge Province occurred chiefly in the Pennsylvanian and Permian periods. This mountain building event, called the Alleghenian Orogeny, is the most recent of the region's four mountain building periods. Paleozoic formations deposited in quieter times folded and faulted into short mountains and are now eroded to expose quartzite backbones. Erosion, numerous limestone quarries and road cuts all help rock and fossil collecting in Pennsylvania's Valley and Ridge Province. Quarries, like those in Winfield and New Paris, delve into thick Silurian and Devonian formations like the Tonoloway, Old Port and Keyser, exposing mineralized seams and fossils. Road cuts in the folded terrain reveal cherts, sphalerite and galena. Borrow pits used for road fill often dig into fossiliferous layers of shale like the extensive Mahantango Formation.

The Great Valley Province in Pennsylvania follows the inner curve of the Valley and Ridge from the Franklin County area to the edge of the Kittatinny Mountains in New Jersey. The Great Valley stretches south from Pennsylvania as far as the Tennessee Valley. Beneath the fertile farm fields of the valley are sedimentary layers of folded and faulted limestone and shale. Like the adjacent Valley and Ridge, the Great Valley contains many caves and caverns. Shale and carbonate layers in the valley weather faster than the surrounding quartzite hills giving the valley its lower elevation.

A small spur of the Blue Ridge Province juts into southern Pennsylvania below the Great Valley. The South Mountain region of Adams County contains exposures of Precambrian metamorphic, igneous and sedimentary rocks. White quartzite, talc, metarhyolite and metabasalt in the Mt. Hope area all belong to this prominent fold structure. Small abandoned copper mines and prospects dot the South Mountain area.

A similar bulge of Precambrian rock called the Reading Prong rests beneath the northeast wing of the Great Valley and blends in with the Highlands Province of New Jersey. Magma intrusions into the Precambrian rock formed metamorphic rocks and minerals like serpentine, tremolite, and diopside.

Physiographic Provinces of Pennsylvania and New Jersey

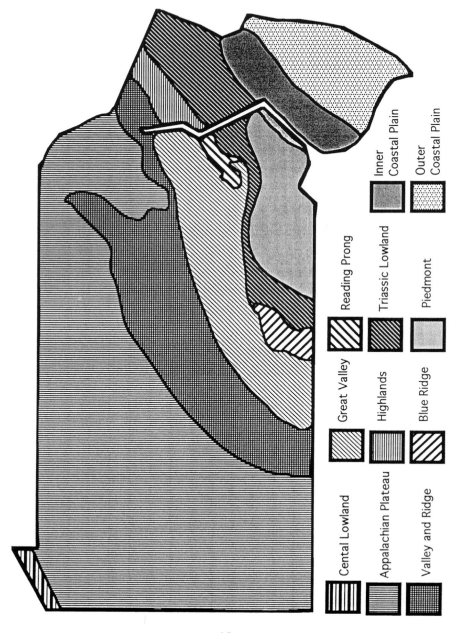

The ridges of the Highlands are broader than those of New Jersey's northernmost province and the valleys are narrow with steep sides. The landscape is predominantly mixed oak forests and contains relic glacial ponds. Rocks of the Highlands are the oldest in New Jersey, but contain few fossils. Zinc mine dumps and quarries in the Franklin Marble Formation are among the world's great mineral collecting locations. New Jersey can rightly boast of its dazzling fluorescent minerals and endless variety of mineral species recorded from these rocks.

The Triassic Lowland, Conestoga Valley and Piedmont Provinces cover the southeast corner of Pennsylvania. These provinces cross into the broad strip of Triassic Lowland and Piedmont of New Jersey. The seaward-tilting Triassic Lowland is an area of red Triassic shale. The red shale of both states reveals the fossil footprints of dinosaurs, reptiles and amphibians. Throughout the Triassic Lowland of Pennsylvania are occasional igneous rock intrusions. Igneous rock on the New Jersey side is much more pronounced. The Triassic was a period of tectonic plate divergence as the supercontinent Pangaea began to break up and the proto-Atlantic Ocean formed. Massive flood basalts cover portions of New Jersey in the Watchung Mountain region. Basalt called "trap rock" is quarried today, revealing highly mineralized layers prized by collectors.

Rifting formed extensive sedimentary basins. Water percolating from lower diabase rock carried copper sulfides into upper sandstone formations. New Jersey copper mines are the oldest mines in the country and many explored the Triassic sandstone for blue-green copper treasure. The most successful New Jersey copper mine was the Schuyler Copper Mine near the New York border where copper minerals can still be found.

Piedmont areas contain extensively metamorphosed igneous and sedimentary rock and contain some of the best gem minerals of Pennsylvania. Within mixtures of gneiss, schist and quartzite are red almandine garnets like those exposed in the Wissahickon Valley and kyanite near Prospect Park. Chromite crystals weather from serpentine rocks into placer streams south of Philadelphia. Other weathered serpentine forms a distinct soil chemistry called serpentine barrens that harbor some of Pennsylvania's most endangered plant life. The Piedmont dips under the coastal plain at Philadelphia and makes only a token appearance on the surface of New Jersey in the Trenton area.

A sliver of land on the southern Pennsylvania banks of the Delaware River marks the beginning of the wide Coastal Plain Province that covers half of New Jersey. Geologists divide the coastal plain into a narrow inner plain and broad outer plain. A sloping sand ridge or cuesta separates the two sections. The inner coastal plain contains the most interesting fossils found in the Garden State. Streams and cuts in the landscape expose Cretaceous age sediments of sand, clay and marl.

In 1858, William Foulke reopened a farmer's marl pit and unearthed the first dinosaur skeleton discovered in the United States in Haddonfield, New Jersey. The discovery of a hadrosaur dinosaur was only one of many fossil discoveries, both vertebrate and invertebrate, that continue from the state's Cretaceous sediments. Fossil collectors regularly prowl the stream banks of New Jersey looking for the signs of ancient life. Two prominent collecting locations are Poricy Brook and Big Brook in Monmouth County.

Cretaceous formations, such as the Magothy exposed near Cliffwood Beach, also contain abundant nodules of marcasite and pyrite. Amber is occasionally reported from related sediments. In 1966, a 90-million-year-old piece of sequoia amber found near Cliffwood Beach held the unique fossil remains of an ant. The ant provided a critical link for scientists to the evolution of ants from their wasp-like relatives. Exciting fossil finds such as these continue to attract fossil hunters to New Jersey.

The outer coastal plain is covered by the most recent of New Jersey's sediments. It also holds New Jersey's last great forest ecosystem—the Pine Barrens. The Pine Barrens of New Jersey spread out for nearly a million acres from Medford to the sea and as far down as Cape May on the southern tip. Today Pine Barrens land ranges from 50 to 150 feet above sea level, though that was not always the case. Sea water covered the area as little as 5 million years ago.

Beneath the sandy, acidic soil of the Pine Barrens, water deposits limonite in sandstone to form bog iron, a low grade iron ore. Although it is not much of an economic importance now, bog iron once fueled a thriving iron industry in the pines 200 years ago.

The Delaware River separating New Jersey and Pennsylvania carries sediments from as far away as New York to the shores of Delaware Bay on the coastal plain. Collectors search the Delaware Bay shores for jasper and fossils carried by the Delaware River. Clear tumbled quartz pebbles know as "Cape May Diamonds" are a favorite of summer tourists visiting Cape May.

TOOLS

Typical tools of collectors include a rock hammer, eye protection, gloves, chisel, awl, map, backpack or bucket, newspaper or foil for wrapping specimens, and small plastic bags or containers. A hard hat and steel-toe boots are sometimes a good idea if there is a danger of falling objects and they may be required on visits to operating quarries. Special equipment or techniques needed for a specific collecting location are noted within the text and instructions for building a screen box for use in stream collecting is in the appendix.

Another tool on a collecting trip is this book. We designed the maps, photographs and instructions in the book to help collectors find and begin an enjoyable day's collecting. Details on the maps are sometimes exaggerated to help collectors locate the proper area. Mileage may vary slightly with the odometers of different vehicles. A detailed road atlas is always helpful in unfamiliar terrain.

RESPONSIBLE COLLECTING

Almost every mineral collecting publication contains a section about "collecting etiquette" and for a good reason. More good collecting locations than we can list have been lost because of poor judgment, thoughtless actions or unsafe behavior by collectors. The low relief and geographic location of much of Pennsylvania and New Jersey make it part of the most densely populated region in the country. Urban and suburban sprawl has also lead to the loss of many collecting locations. Collecting sites that remain are a true treasure and their loss due to unfortunate collecting practices would be a tragedy for collectors. The gold rush days are gone and it is time for collectors to safeguard their hobby for the future.

Collectors who have visited western states may be familiar with vast tracts of public lands that are, at present, still open and friendly to recreational collectors. Space is much more limited in the East and there is much more competition for those sites that are open to collectors. As a result, the availability of collecting sites often depends solely on the goodwill of an individual or organization. Use common sense when collecting and respect the property of the land owner. Do not trespass in areas that are off-limits.

Common sense is especially important with regard to quarries and other potentially hazardous locations. Quarries and mining operations may present extreme danger to unwary collectors and many locations are entirely unsuited for children. Never enter an active or private quarry without the knowledge of the owner. Fortunately, some of the best quarries have open house days set aside specifically for collectors. Obey all quarry rules when entering a quarry and stay away from all machinery and quarry walls. Safety is always paramount. Abuse of collecting privileges or unsafe behavior by collectors can cause such days to disappear.

We selected the collecting locations listed in the book for their minerals and availability. The status of the land or the ownership may change at any time. Mention of the collecting location in this book does not automatically give you permission to collect. If the conditions at a site look different from described, check before entering. Keeping your collecting trips safe and responsible is the best way to enjoy a collecting trip and keep our hobby alive for future collectors.

SHELOCTA SIDERITE CONCRETIONS ____

The extensive sedimentary deposits of western Pennsylvania make many possible collecting localities for siderite nodules. Siderite frequently occurs in deposits of clay, coal seams, or shale in its massive or concretion form. A good locality for siderite concretions is near Shelocta on a former stream bank of Crooked Creek. The siderite, an iron carbonate, is found with platy barite, sphalerite, and the sphalerite variety wurtzite. This locality is the first wurtzite occurrence discovered in western Pennsylvania.

According to a Pennsylvania State Geological Survey publication, the concretions formed under marine conditions in the Pennsylvanian age, about 300 million years ago. They were formed prior to lithification of the enclosing sediment, which means before it became rock. During or after lithification, shrinkage cracks formed in the concretions. These cracks later filled with the minerals that probably precipitated from ground water.

The bed containing the smooth, oval or round, brown nodules is above the Bush Creek limestone of the Glenshaw Formation. Look for the rock layer just above the yellow-orange staining on the formation. Many nodules fall out of this layer and they are easy to pick up from the ground or roadside at the base of the 35-foot high embankment. It is more difficult and more hazardous trying to climb to the nodule-rich layer.

While the nodules or concretions are fascinating by themselves, it is more fun to pretend they are presents and open them. A couple of light taps with a rock hammer tell you immediately if you have anything interesting inside. If they do not pop open right away, they lack visible minerals. The nodules open conveniently at the barite crystals, exposing the clear, shiny circular plates. Use a hand lens to find the sphalerite or wurtzite embedded in either the barite or in the siderite nodule itself.

To get to this locality, take U.S. Highway 422 from Indiana, Pennsylvania. Turn north onto Wood Road, which is 0.5 mile west of the U.S. Highway 422 junction with State Highway 156 in Shelocta. The embankment is 0.1 mile from U.S. Highway 422 on the left side of the road. Park on the right, well off the road. It may look like a back country road, but it is surprisingly busy.

Hammer, safety glasses, and a hand lens are your only equipment needs. Keep your eyes open for fossils, too. Small gastropods, such as *Meekospira*, are commonly found weathered out of the formation.

Shelocta Siderite Concretions

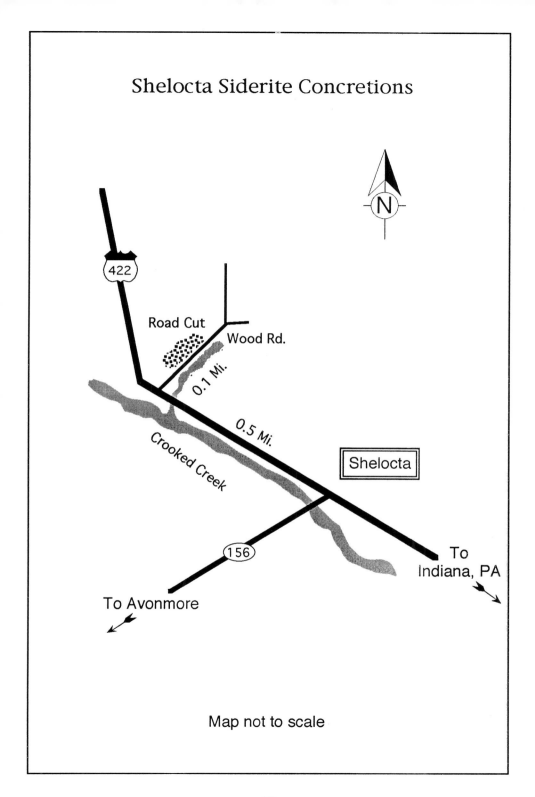

site 2 NEW PARIS FLUORITE

The quarry in New Paris, Pennsylvania, owned by the New Enterprise Stone & Lime Co., Inc. is a rich source of calcite, fossils, and deep purple, green and yellow fluorite. The road to the quarry entrance is about 1.0 mile northeast of New Paris on State Highway 96. The road is not well marked with street signs. It is on the right just before a barn. There is a covered bridge, also on the right, a short distance past the turn. After turning onto the road follow it 0.4 mile and turn left. The quarry entrance is another 0.2 mile at the caretaker's house. Collectors need to make advance arrangements with the owners before entering the site.

Collectors are likely to first find massive calcite as they begin to explore the quarry. Veins of calcite radiate through the limestone and contain cavities of calcite crystals. In addition to short terminated calcite crystals, the quarry produces small bladed crystals and squat barrel-like calcite crystals half-an-inch wide or larger. Some cavities of calcite from the quarry also fluoresce and phosphoresce green under short-wave ultraviolet light.

Fluorite occurs in the same veins as the calcite. Purple fluorite is the most common color with crystals averaging one-eighth to one-quarter inch wide. Cubes of fluorite as large as one inch wide were reported during the quarry's active years. Fluorite may turn up anywhere in the quarry, but is most prolific in areas near the front of the quarry where the calcite veins are closely laminated horizontally in the limestone. Searching the bedded limestone has the feel of splitting shale for fossils. Calcite veins in the laminated limestone are only one to two inches wide. The fluorite crystals show through on the broken side of the vein. After cracking a piece of fluorite-bearing calcite, it is difficult to expose the mineral further without losing the brittle fluorite.

According to the Pennsylvania Geological Survey, limestone containing fluorite at the quarry may be part of the Silurian-Devonian Keyser Formation. Huge blocks of limestone containing brachiopods have tumbled from upper layers onto the northeast side of the terrace surrounding the quarry bottom.

To get permission to enter the quarry contact Mr. Birch Snider at New Enterprise Stone & Lime Co. in Ashcom at (814) 652-5121 in advance of your trip. You will need to sign a liability release before entering the quarry. A hard hat, long pants and safety glasses are also advisable.

New Paris Fluorite

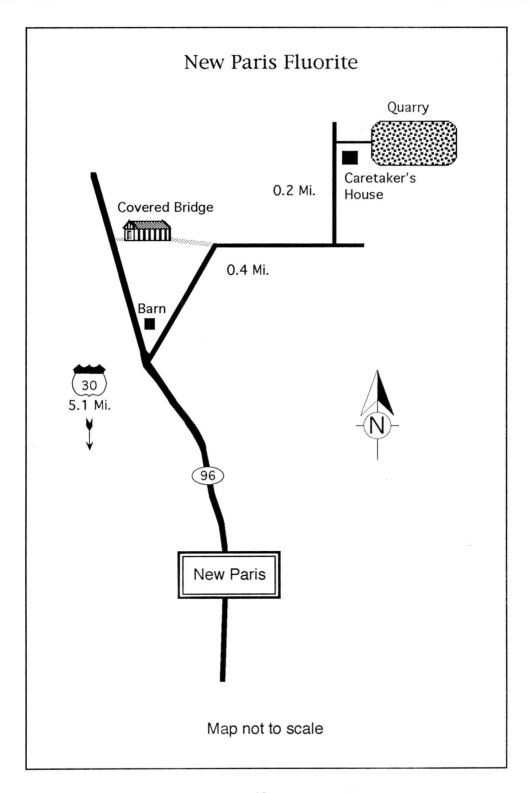

Map not to scale

NEW ENTERPRISE BANDED CHERT _____

Chert is not usually an eagerly desired stone, but some interesting banded chert nodules are present at a road cut about 1.25 miles east of the village of New Enterprise in Bedford County, Pennsylvania on State Highway 869. The village of New Enterprise should not be confused with the many area quarries of the same name. The location lies on the western edge of Pennsylvania's Valley and Ridge Province in an area known as Morrison Cove. Morrison Cove is a large valley resting between the Dunning, Evitts and Tussey Mountains roughly 12 miles north of Bedford. The easiest way to find the road cut is to drive 0.4 miles west from the intersection of State Highways 869 and 36. The shoulder at the road cut is too narrow for parking so you will need to drive by it to park.

Look for the banded nodules on the north side of the road near the center of the road cut in an area about 20 yards wide. The chert area is not wide because it follows a thin layer in the limestone at a steep angle up from the road rather than horizontally. Dark to light gray cherts are in the roadside rubble and in the steeply-dipped layers of the host limestone/dolomite. The best way to locate the cherty layer is to look for broken bits of chert at the bottom of the slope and follow it upward to the source. Plants and brush can make this part a bit difficult during the summer. The banded chert is usually dark gray with concentric circles of white. It is good for either tumbling or as cutting material. Typical nodules are from two to five inches long.

Small traces of sphalerite are also present in the road cut along with small dolomite crystals near the western edge of the cut. An ash-colored slag is present at spots along the road cut. Although the frothy slag appears to contain speckles of metallic minerals and

fluoresces under short-wave ultraviolet light, the material is probably a waste slag from one of the many iron furnaces that were once in production.

Collecting at the steep road cut.

New Enterprise Banded Chert

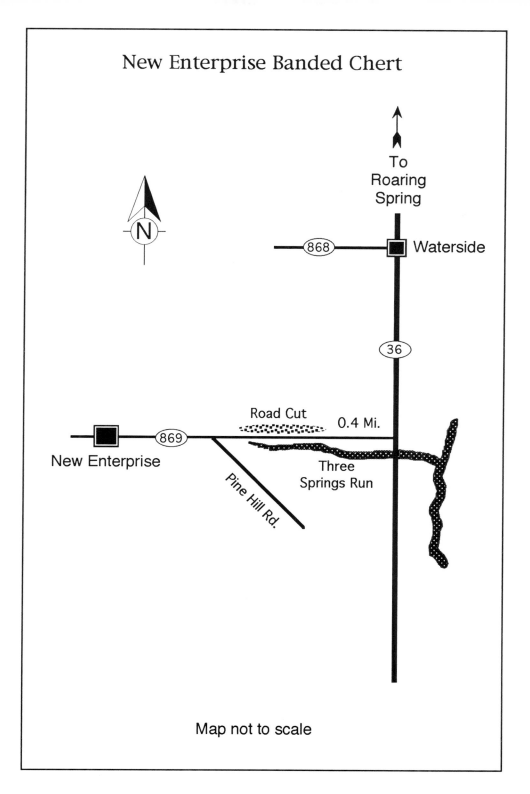

ROARING SPRING QUARTZ & CHERT

A grab bag of banded cherty stones reside in a small wash behind a road cut 100 yards south of the intersection of State Highway 867 (West Main St.) and State Highway 36 in Roaring Spring, Pennsylvania. There is a small pullover on the south side of State Highway 867. The collecting area is adjacent to an active quarry containing dolomitic rock of the Bellefonte Formation and it is likely that the road contains much of the same material.

Silica replaces portions of the dolomite, forming nodules of jasper-like quartz and chert that weathers from the formation. The best nodule hunting is in a small wash that opens on the east side of the road opposite the entrance to State Highway 867. The wash runs behind the entire length of the road cut. Obviously, low water will be an asset for searching the wash.

Pieces of jasper-like quartz and nodules up to five inches in diameter or more are bluish gray and may not stand out from the gray dolomite at first. Pick up and examine suspected nodules. A close inspection will usually differentiate quartz nodules from the surrounding dolomite despite a reddish coating of limonite. Nodules of chert and dolomite are about the same size as the quartz nodules. Gray to white cherty stones may contain concentric bands or unusual swirls. Some of the swirls resemble comets with long tails streaking through the rock.

Sphalerite exposed in the active quarry is also present to a lesser degree in the road cut. The hills of Pennsylvania have eyes, but not very impressive eyes where sphalerite is concerned. Sphalerite appears as dots, sometimes known as sphalerite "eyes," in certain layers of the dolomite. The eyes are easiest to see in rock exposed on the road cut.

State Highway 36 is a busy and noisy highway with tremendous truck traffic from area quarries. The site is not a good location to take children and anyone must use caution when walking along the steep walls of the road cut.

The road cut borders a busy highway.

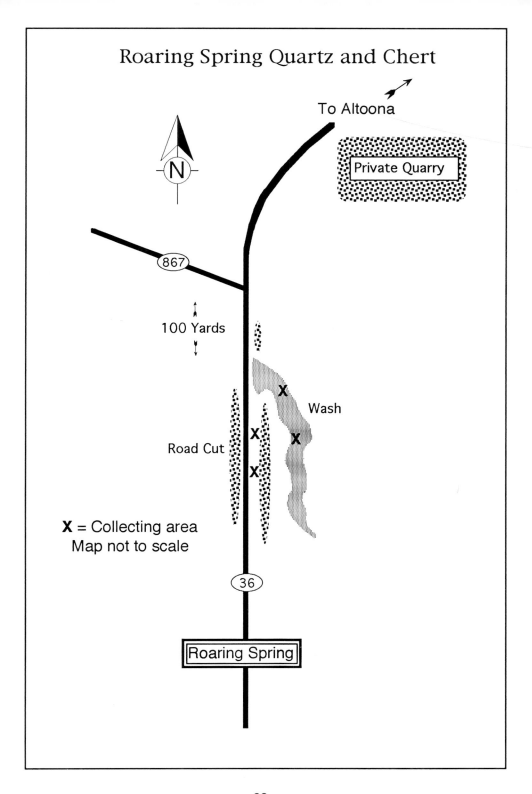

Roaring Spring Quartz and Chert

To Altoona

Private Quarry

N

867

100 Yards

Wash

Road Cut

X

X

X

X

X = Collecting area
Map not to scale

36

Roaring Spring

In a most unlikely spot, there is a rock most unlikely to be collected. It is a shale concretion as big as a truck and it sits in a junk yard. The concretion is a favorite rock of many people, so please be kind to it.

The folks at Tyrone Auto Salvage do not quite understand people's fascination with their large concretions, but they are kind to them, too. They move the rocks around with a front-end loader when they are in the way. Otherwise, they are tolerant of the rocks and the people who ask to look at them.

At the rear of the junk yard is a 10- to 20-foot high exposure through the shale formation out of which these concretions fall. The formation is the Marcellus shale of Middle Devonian age, about 380 million years old. The concretions formed prior to the shale's lithification from the shallow seas.

Mineralization developed in shrinkage cracks that are concentric to the wide diameter of the concretion. Occasionally minerals formed on the lateral joint cracks. The minerals in and on the concretions include limonite staining of the exterior, several forms of calcite, barite crystals, small pyrite crystals, and dolomite. Phillipsite, a zeolite, is white or reddish in color, and monoclinic in form. It is reported by several collectors and confirmed by testing done on concretions at a similar site. No other zeolites, which are hydrous silicates, are reported. The presence of strontianite is suspected, but unconfirmed.

This site is private property and permission must be obtained from the auto salvage manager, Bob Stager. While on the property, you must respect the company's need to conduct business and not interfere with their activities.

You can wander as far along the exposure as you wish. Look for medium-sized concretions up to 3 feet in diameter. They tumble out of the exposure and are at the base. Pieces of concretions cracked by weathering are easily found. There are enough broken pieces, with visible minerals, to satisfy your collecting needs. There is no need to break up the biggest of the concretions.

There is enough to do here by taking a picture of the grandfather of concretions, checking out the calcite and looking for unsubstantiated strontianite.

Call Tyrone Auto Salvage for permission at (814) 684-0310 or write Bob Stager at RD #5, Box 50, Tyrone, PA 16686. To find the place, take U.S. Highway 220 from Altoona to Grazierville. From the bypass, exit at Grazierville. From the U.S. Highway 220 connection at S. R. 4027, it is 0.5 mile to the auto salvage on the right. If you cross the large bridge over the railroad tracks, you have gone too far.

Grazierville Shale Concretions

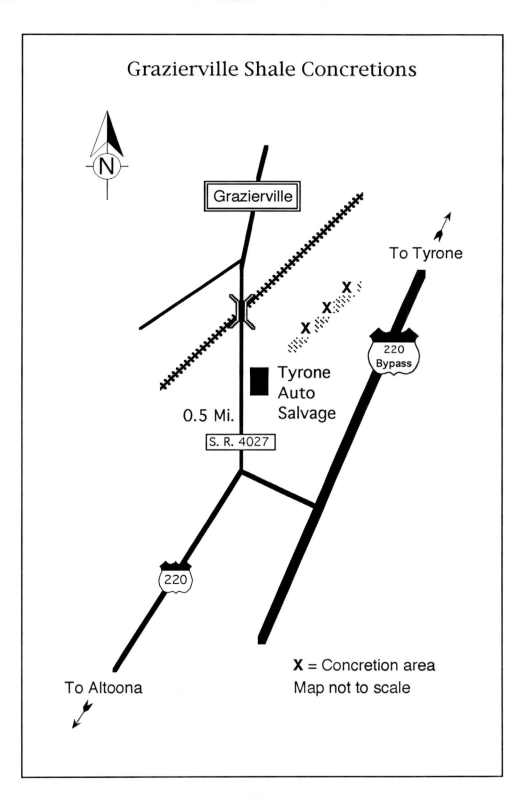

CALIFORNIA QUARRIES

The former limestone quarries near Tyrone, Pennsylvania still contain calcite finds for the lucky collector. Joseph Gurekovich is the present owner of California Quarries, named in memory of the immigrants fooled into believing they were going to mine gold. He recently purchased this land to preserve its human history, wildlife habitat, and environmental beauties.

The four quarries are parallel to Elk Run, a small stream that flows into the Little Juniata River. Limestone mined in the California Quarries from the 1700s until the mid-1900s was considered the best quality limestone in the country. It was used as flux in steel mills, for building the first roads, and was burned to make lime for agricultural purposes.

To reach the area, travel southeast from Tyrone on State Highway 453 for about 1.0 mile. Soon after the intersection of State Highway 45, look for an entrance to S.R. 1015 on the left side of the road. The road will lead back under the highway and continue by the town of Ironville. In order to go to the quarries, you must contact Mr. Gurekovich at R.D. 1 Box 27, Tyrone, PA 16686-9501 to arrange a supervised visit. His family is working hard to reclaim the land after many years of former owners' neglect and misuse, including outrageous trash dumping. Please be patient with your touring requests.

The first of the four quarries is near the lime kilns, and has a cliff face that extends about 400 feet high. From here you can see remains of the Pennsylvania Railroad line and a bridge across Elk Run. Calcite crystals are in seams and vugs in the limestone rubble by the quarry walls. Poorly preserved marine fossils are also present in some of the limestone. Some of the fossils appear to be burrows of marine organisms. These trace fossils separate in broad sheets from the surrounding limestone.

A towering limestone wall extends from the second to the third quarries. The third quarry has become a natural wetland, filled with willow trees and brambles, and is an ideal wildlife habitat. Search for clear or yellow calcite crystals and massive calcite in the smaller walls surrounding the swampy areas. The fourth quarry is filled by artesian wells and is 35 feet deep.

Visitors to California Quarries must respect the work in progress and ask permission to collect. The Gurekovich family asks that you have a valid Eastern Federation of Mineralogical Clubs and Lapidary Societies membership to indicate you have adequate insurance for collecting. Enjoy the beauty of this place and appreciate the vision of a man who loves the land in which he was raised.

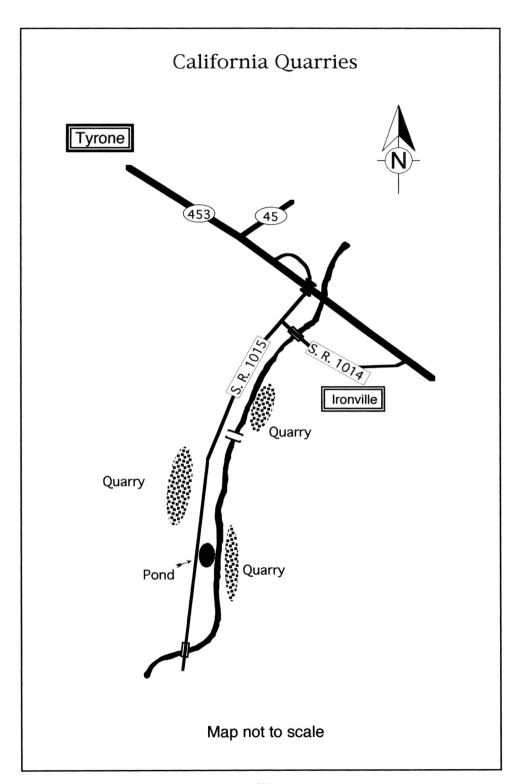

California Quarries

Map not to scale

Checking concretions for barite and siderite near Shelocta.

Picking through the quarry rubble outside of the town of New Paris.

A gigantic concretion at the junk yard near Grazierville.

A view of a quarry and wetland in California Quarries.

HUNTINGDON FOSSILS

In western Pennsylvania small malls and a variety of retail shops are wedged into narrow roadside strips cut out of the shale and coal-rich rock. It is occasionally productive to stop at such places. Spend a few minutes walking around the rear of the buildings. Looking at samples of the rock might lead you to a rich discovery.

One such locality which proved worthwhile is in Huntingdon. The site is opposite a Days Inn beside the busy and accessible U. S. Highway 22. Fossils and minerals are both found in this location. A collector can hardly ask for more.

The road cut exposes 300-million-year-old shale. At the northern end of the cut are larger quantities of good marine fossils, primarily brachiopods. Toward the southern end, the mineral siderite is more abundant.

Siderite nodules, or concretions are an iron carbonate. You might hear others call them iron stone concretions. The nodules are oval or round, mostly fist-sized, and dark brown. The concretions formed in the marine conditions of the Pennsylvanian period, before the sediments became rock. Platy barite is commonly precipitated inside the nodules and can be found by breaking them in half. Nodules crack open along the mineral deposition area with a tap of a rock hammer.

Bivalves and brachiopods are common finds in the dark gray shale of the road cut. As in other counties on the Appalachian Plateau, massive sedimentary beds provide many opportunities to look for the perfect collection specimen.

To get to the site, drive almost 2.7 miles south of the intersection of State Highway 26 and U. S. Highway 22. The parking area is immediately after the diagonal road entering U. S. Highway 22 from the right.

The nodules and fossils conveniently weather out of the 10 to 20-foot high cliff. A leisurely walk along the length of the road cut will yield specimens. You need to bring only a bucket or bag and your good eyes. If you decide to tap into the siderite concretions, bring a hammer and eye protection. Please refrain from climbing the road cuts in these locations.

A mass of marine fossils from the site.

The survival of this site is problematic. However, it is important for the collector in Pennsylvania to recognize this kind of opportunity and to take advantage of it when it occurs. Recent construction threatens to overwhelm this fossil location, but look for other area cuts and new construction that may reveal similar fossils.

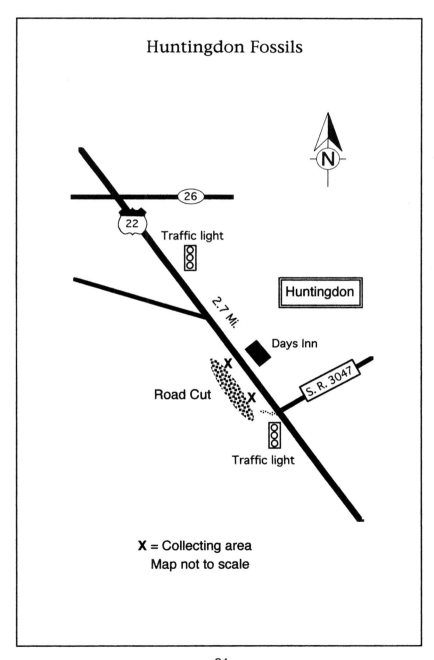

Huntingdon Fossils

X = Collecting area
Map not to scale

MAPLETON GALENA

Lead deposits in the Sinking Valley region of Pennsylvania were once a critical asset in colonial America. Fort Roberdeau, constructed in Sinking Valley during the Revolutionary War, protected the valuable lead mines. A reconstructed Fort Roberdeau is now open to the public at the fort's original site. Unfortunately, a fire destroyed the collection of local minerals once housed at the museum.

Today, most of the early lead mines are either lost or hidden away on private land. One outcrop of galena and other minerals, however, is still readily accessible roughly 20 miles southeast of Sinking Valley on U.S. Highway 22 near Mapleton. Although not mined except by recreational collectors, the road cut can provide a sampling of what the early miners discovered in Sinking Valley.

The outcrop is about 2.8 miles north of U.S. Highway 22's intersection with S. R. 522 at Mount Union or 0.3 mile south of Motel 22 on U.S. Highway 22. There is a parking area next to a dirt road just south of the road cut. Traffic on Highway 22 can be heavy and care should be taken while turning into the parking area from either direction. Private land borders the road, but the minerals occur in the highway right of way. Traffic makes this road cut a poor area for children. Adults should also be careful not to back into oncoming traffic while admiring a sparkling specimen of galena.

Collectors will probably first notice Tuscarora quartzite as they walk along the road cut. This Silurian rock looks as if it is half quartzite and half sandstone. The Tuscarora Formation contacts the Rose Hill shale in the area of the cut. Pennsylvania Geological Survey publications indicate that hydrothermal solutions deposited minerals like galena and sphalerite after the two formations were joined by faulting.

Walking farther up the road you can find specimens of drusy quartz crystals in vugs and farther still, an area where collectors have been at work by the roadside. Flashes of silvery galena, golden pyrite and quartz are fairly obvious in the broken rock. Hidden galena can easily be found by hefting the rocks for the dense mineral. Samples of massive galena of more than a pound still come from the road cut. Be careful not to let rocks fall onto the roadway at the bottom of the slope. There is not much room on the shoulder there for you, the cars or the rocks.

A number of microcrystals have also been recorded by the state geologic survey at this location including red, orange, yellow, brown and black sphalerite, chalcopyrite, anglesite (white coatings on the galena), and something with the unlikely name of plumbojarosite, a yellow-brown galena coating.

Mapleton Galena

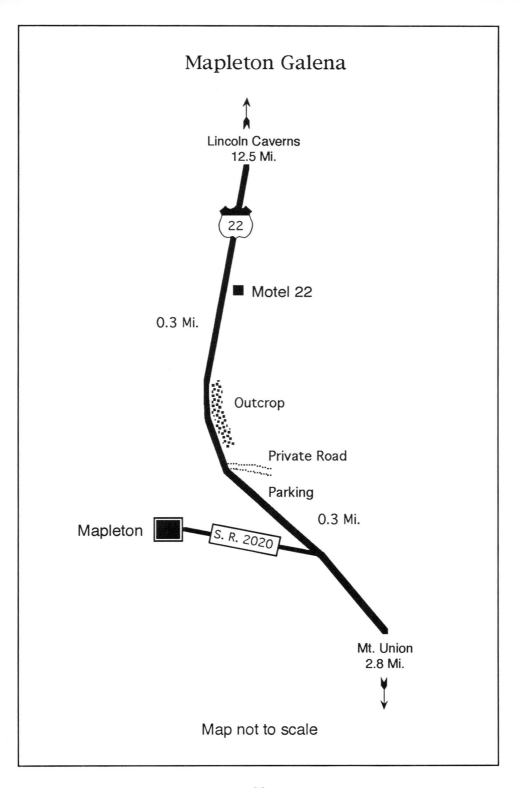

Lincoln Caverns
12.5 Mi.

22

■ Motel 22

0.3 Mi.

Outcrop

Private Road

Parking

0.3 Mi.

Mapleton ■ S. R. 2020

Mt. Union
2.8 Mi.

Map not to scale

ICKESBURG TRILOBITES

West of Bloomfield or New Bloomfield, depending on the map you use, and near the town of Ickesburg, Pennsylvania is an outcrop of Mahantango Formation shale. The shale is rich in Middle Devonian Age fossils. The outcrop is a shale pit, sometimes called Smith's shale pit in other literature. It is used as a borrow pit, and is located behind a Saville township building.

Strata exposed in the pit ranges from a dark gray shale that crumbles easily on the bottom, through mudstone, to a very hard calcareous limestone and sandstone on the top. The typical Mahantango formation is the mudstone with large concretions. Fossils are found in all the strata.

Start by poking around the crumbly shale at the bottom. Hands are the only tools needed here. Some large trilobites and tabulate coral pieces are found in the crumbly shale. Walk uphill into the pit. The sides of the pit are the hard mudstone. Use a pick or hammer to break apart the shale. While brachiopods, pelecypods, and bryozoans are abundant, trilobites are the choice specimens. Look for *Phacops rana, Greenops boothi, Dipleura dekayi,* and *Basidechenella kayseri.* Do not ignore rocks that have fallen off the pit walls. You might find yourself standing on a well-preserved, whole trilobite. Fossils are also found by breaking apart the hard sandstone layer near the top.

Besides your rock hammer and a small pick, eye protection is necessary. If you are collecting with a group, wear a hard hat and watch out for those collecting above and below you. This is a favorite location for groups, recommended by the Perry County Tourist and Recreation department. Since the fossils are fragile, bring plenty of wrapping paper and small bags for protection of your specimens.

The township building is on State Highway 74 about 4.0 miles north of the intersection with State Highway 274. While you are in the area, do not overlook the chance to inspect other borrow pits that are not posted. You must have permission from private property owners; please do not trespass.

Ickesburg Trilobites

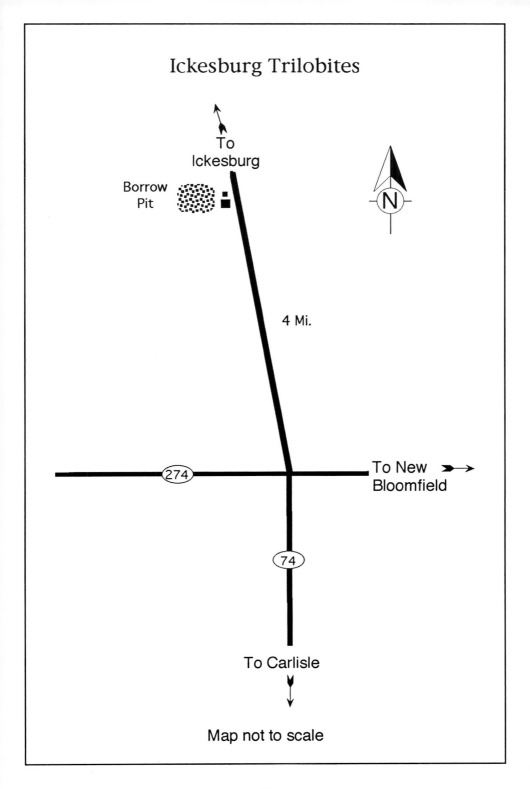

NEW BLOOMFIELD DEVONIAN FOSSILS ‗

The sea that covered central Pennsylvania in Middle Devonian times was home to abundant marine organisms. Fine-grained sediments deposited on the sea floor about 385 million years ago produced the clay and lime shales of the Mahantango Formation in modern-day Perry County.

A large shale pit provides collecting opportunities for marine invertebrates. Shale in the pit is rich with fossil brachiopods, bivalves, trilobites, corals, and bryozoans. The dark shale is so brittle that minimum equipment pries it apart easily. Hands and a screwdriver are usually all that is needed, though a rock hammer and eye protection come in handy when dealing with large pieces. You will also want to have paper for wrapping the fragile specimens so they do not break in transport.

The pit is located 100 yards off State Highway 34 on Township Road T-361 or Roth Road. Roth Road is 0.5 mile south of New Bloomfield, also called Bloomfield, depending on the map you use. A suitable parking area is on the right, opposite the pit. There is a long winding road to the top of the pit, but leave your car in the parking area. Fossils are everywhere, but so are broken glass and other by-products of unthinking consumerism. Avoid the steep walls of the pit. There are plenty of rocks to turn over. You will probably find that you do not even have to walk all the way up to the top of the pit to find enough fossils to fill your bag.

Characteristic specimens of the Middle Devonian period include coral *Favosites*, bryozoan *Fenestrella*, brachiopods *Mucrospirifer*,

Megastrophia, and *Spinatrypa*, and gastropod *Platyceras*. Pelecypods and unidentified fragments of trilobites are plentiful. Finding an exhaustive list of fossils is possible by thoroughly searching this shale pit.

Collecting at the borrow pit is easy.

36

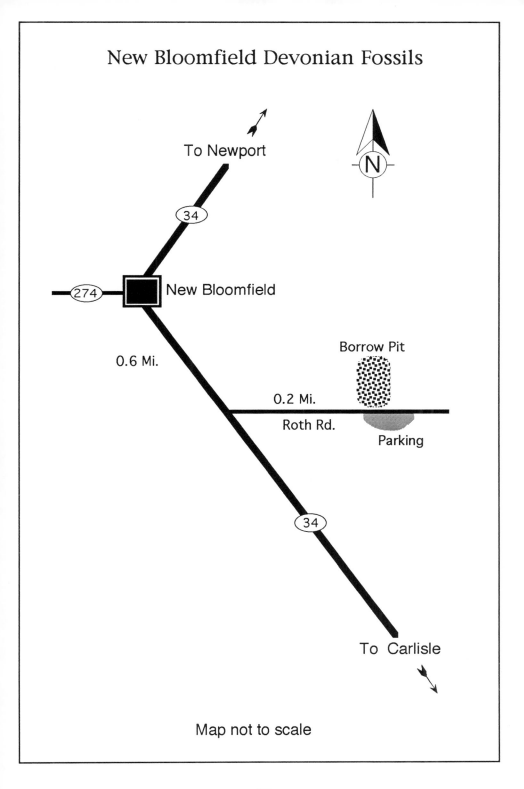

New Bloomfield Devonian Fossils

To Newport

N

34

274 New Bloomfield

0.6 Mi.

0.2 Mi.

Roth Rd.

Borrow Pit

Parking

34

To Carlisle

Map not to scale

MT. HOPE WHITE QUARTZITE

An old quarry at Mt. Hope, Pennsylvania, southwest of Gettysburg, contains thick veins of bright white quartzite and talc. The tiny town of Mt. Hope, is about 3.0 miles from the intersection of Mt. Hope Road with State Highway 116 or 3.3 miles from the intersection of Mt. Hope Road with Gum Springs Road in the south. The quarry is about 200 feet east of the church in Mt. Hope.

Quartzite at Mt. Hope is bright white with an almost marble-like appearance. The hard quartzite is a fine material for either tumbling or cutting. Polished slabs display cloud-like patterns and lines within. While the quartzite is an attractive stone when polished, its white color and relative abundance may make it a useful secondary stone to highlight more colorful stones and gems in lapidary projects.

Geologic formations in the Mt. Hope area consist largely of metabasalt, metarhyolite, phyllite, quartzite and other metamorphic rocks. An active mine at Greenstone still quarries the green metamorphic rock, called greenstone, for use in roofing shingles. Mineralized veins bearing copper also surface throughout the region. Many small mines and prospects opened nearby hoping for a big copper strike that never materialized. Speculators once believed that area mines would be as successful in copper production as those in Michigan.

The remains of the Becktel Copper Mine are directly across the road from the quarry. A small pond now fills the pit and shaft next to the road. If the area remains unposted, it may be worthwhile to look in the gravel and stones of Middle Creek that flows nearby for a sample of copper ore or other minerals.

The road cuts through a small embankment immediately east of the quarry exposing a layer of talc. The white silky-feeling mineral is the same material used to make talcum powder. Talc, sometimes known as soapstone, is used for carving, though the quality here is questionable.

A little farther east of the quarry on Mt. Hope Road is the Strawberry Hill Nature Center. The staff are helpful and polite and have a number of geologic publications at their disposal. The nature center also has a small, but useful display of area minerals.

Mt. Hope White Quartzite

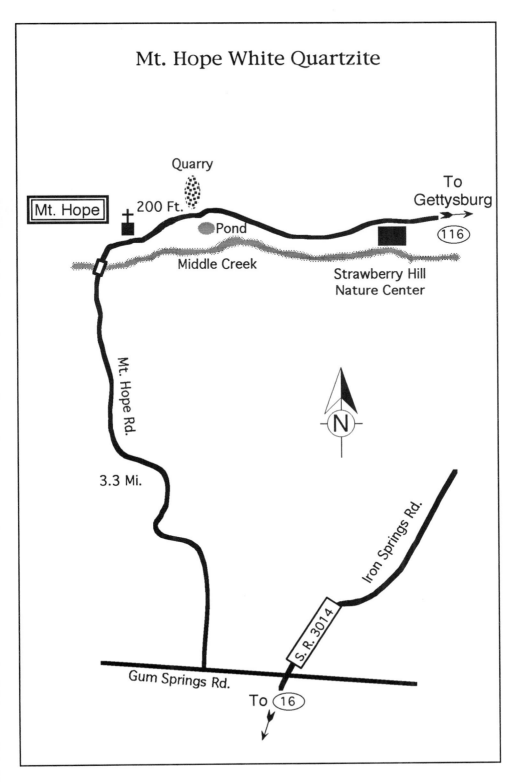

Bright white quartzite found at the old quarry at Mt. Hope.

A cut piece of quartzite from the Mt. Hope quarry.

MT. HOLLY SPRINGS AGATE _____

While agate sites in Pennsylvania are few, Mt. Holly Springs, south of Carlisle, remains a productive location for collectors. Nodules in the farm fields near the town have colors ranging from a reddish brown to an attractive blue-gray. The agate occurs in fields on either side of West Pine Street and along the small creek that runs through the property. Geologists believe the nodules weathered out from the Cambrian Age Tomstown Dolomite and are brought to the surface by plowing.

The typical agate is the blue-gray variety with distinctive lines or veins radiating from the center. Although a dull orange rind covers the agate, repeated plowing has broken many of the larger nodules to reveal the interior. Egg-sized chunks to nodules more than a foot in diameter are fairly common after a plowing. The blue-gray agate nodules are excellent slabbing material. Fractures in the agate cause it to crack during more specific cutting for cabochons so the cutter needs a little patience to work the stone.

Small sphere-like nodules are more likely to contain darker colors or swirling fortification agate similar to many western agates. These small nodules are scarce, but perfect for tumbling. The rind disappears in about a day of coarse tumbling and the agate takes a smooth polish. Large nodules of the dense red-brown mineral goethite are also common in the area.

To reach the collecting area take State Highway 34 south through Mt. Holly Springs and turn west onto West Pine Street. Drive approximately 1.2 miles to a farm house on the north side of the road. The farm fields are private land and you must get permission from the land owners at the farm house before doing any collecting. The collecting area extends on either side of the road for about 0.25 mile and perhaps another 0.5 mile west.

Under no circumstances should the crops in the fields be disturbed or damaged. Carefully search the fields and stream side, paying close attention to any areas of erosion or piles of rocks at the edges of the field.

Searching farm fields at the collecting site.

41

Mt. Holly Springs Agate

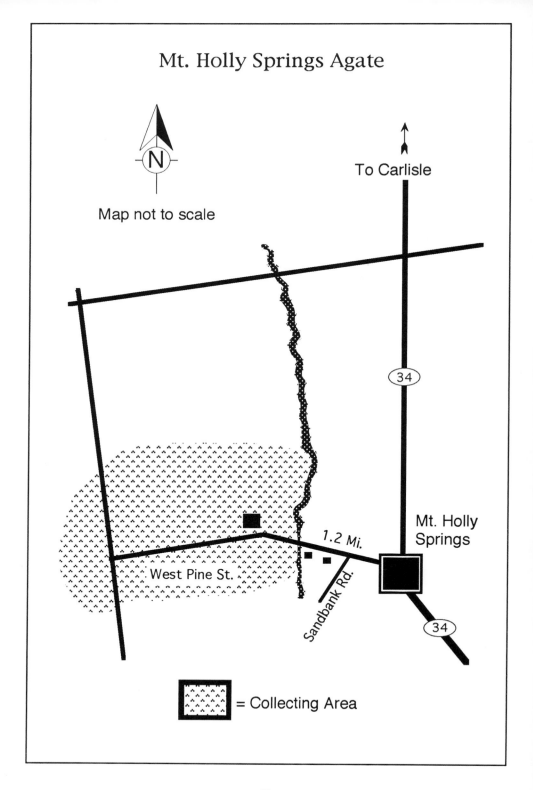

ROSSVILLE COPPER MINERALS

Between Rossville and Dillsburg, Pennsylvania there is a roadside copper mineral occurrence that has been productive for years. The site is not much more than a small cavern, dug by gophers known as mineral collectors. If you would like an easy spot to find a specimen of malachite or a piece of vividly colored azurite, this one is for you.

The malachite is found as green coatings along with blue azurite coatings on fractures in hornfels. This rock, which was once shale, metamorphosed during the Triassic Age. The copper sulfide series of chalcopyrite, bornite, digenite, and chalcocite recently converted into azurite and malachite by near-surface ground waters, according to a Pennsylvania Geological Survey publication.

For a micro-mineral collector, this location offers the possibility of finding chabazite, hematite, heulandite, magnetite, stilbite, epidote, and actinolite in addition to copper minerals. In the same road cut, closer to Rossville, there are reports of white anorthite-bytownite crystals. Most minerals form on the fractures of the rock, so search the cracks and fractures with a hand lens to look for micros. This is not a major strike, but it is an opportunity for some easy copper minerals.

To get to the road cut, take State Highway 74 from the south into Rossville. In the center of town, instead of turning left to continue State Highway 74, go straight on what is now S. R. 4026. You will soon notice a small, mostly grass-covered road cut on the right. In 0.7 mile, the diggings of previous collectors are visible. Park beside them.

The road is a heavily-traveled one, so you must park well off the shoulder of the road for your own protection. Do not block driveways or park in front of any nearby houses. Necessary collecting supplies are few. Bring a small chisel and a hammer, besides a hand lens, if you wish to work at the small diggings. Bring materials to wrap the micro-mount minerals and a bag to carry specimens.

Looking for copper minerals in the road cut.

Rossville Copper Minerals

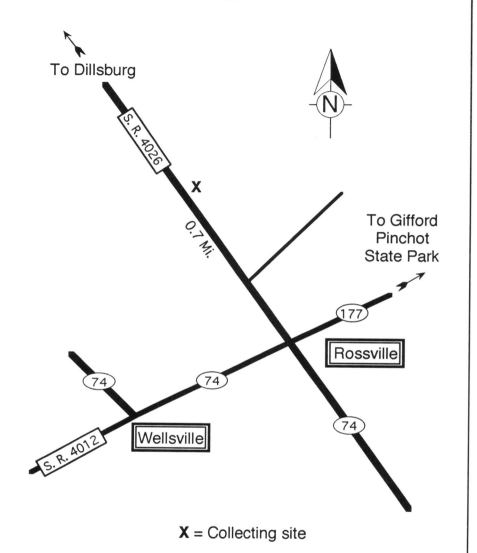

To Dillsburg

S. R. 4026

N

X

0.7 Mi.

To Gifford
Pinchot
State Park

177

Rossville

74

74

74

S. R. 4012

Wellsville

X = Collecting site

Map not to scale

KINZUA DAM FOSSILS

A dramatic road cut on State Highway 59 across from Kinzua Dam in Pennsylvania exposes a cross section of formations in the upper Devonian Conewango Group near an area called the Big Bend. The cut rests on the northern edge of Allegheny National Forest approximately 6.0 miles from State Highway 59's intersection with U.S. Highway 6 near Warren. The best collecting in the exposure is 0.4 mile east of the entrance to the Kinzua Dam Visitor Center and about 0.2 mile before the dam itself.

Fossils of the Verango Formation (once called the Cattaraugus Formation) weather from the shear wall and fall to the cliff base. Collectors can easily spot masses of finely preserved brachiopods and other fossil shells along the roadside. Some brachiopods are nearly as big as your fist. While you may see a complete fossil right away, the first view could also be a much more humble example. Examine the fallen rocks carefully as you walk and don't be afraid to look at them closely. Once you find the first fossil, you will probably find many more in the immediate area.

Many of the fossils occur in a large densely packed shell layer. Occasionally, large sheets of this fossil layer drop from the cliff. Fossil sheets up to three feet or more across are sometimes lying by the roadside. The gracefully winged brachiopod *Cyrtospirifer* is a common find at Kinzua Dam. Some of the fossil sections preserve portions of the shallow prehistoric sea floor just as it once appeared. Dozens to hundreds of fossil animals appear frozen in their life positions perhaps smothered by increased silting millions of years ago.

A layer of sandstone called the Verango Second Sand rests on top of the marine fossil layer. The sandstone probably represents one of the many transitions from shallow Devonian sea to land. Huge blocks of the sandstone lay fallen from the upper portions of the cut across from the dam's parking area.

Rockhounds can trim up their finds on the spot or take specimens home to prepare and free from the shale matrix. In addition to the many invertebrate fossils, you can look for trace fossils of burrowing marine animals. Burrows appear as small tubes or cavities in the shale layers filled with a slightly different colored sediment. Some of the burrows contain tiny siderite crystals.

The walls of the road cut are damp from dripping spring waters and droplets carried from the dam's rushing overflow. A perpetual rainbow mist hangs above the Allegheny River at the dam. Thick moss and algae growing on the wall and rocks makes for slippery footing at times. Of course, there is always the danger of falling rocks near the side of the wall. Please collect with caution here and at all collecting locations.

After collecting, leave some time to explore the dam and the view above the Allegheny River and Reservoir. Additional area information about the dam and forest is available at the visitor center up the road. You might also ask for directions to the scenic loop drive that overlooks the entire Kinzua Pass.

Parked by the Kinzua Dam road cut.

Kinzua Dam Fossils

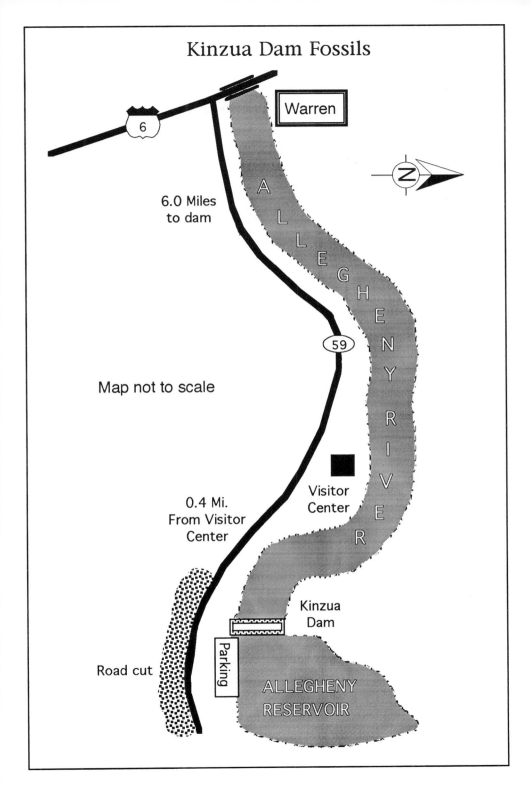

site 15 HIGHLAND PICTURE SANDSTONE

Picture sandstone from Pennsylvania is not something commonly spotted at area rock and gem shows, yet it is there. You can find picture sandstone and plant fossils at a borrow pit located off an unpaved road near the village of Highland (also known as Highland Corners) roughly 20 miles southeast of Warren on State Highway 948.

Follow State Highway 948 3.4 miles southeast from S. R. 4009 at Highland and look for Forest Road 143 leading south. The road number is marked on a wooden post. Autumn colors along this road are especially vibrant if you happen to be lucky enough to be there on a sunny fall day. Travel 3.9 miles to a dirt track on the right side of the road along Red Mill Run. You will cross a power line cut 0.6 mile before reaching Red Mill Run. The borrow pit is a 0.25 mile walk up the track opposite the stream.

Look for the best picture stone and plant fossils near the base of the amphitheater-like pit where the blocks of sandstone and rubble are heaviest. Select sandstone with darker iron stains and veins of limonite in it. You will need to imagine how the dusty rough chunks will look after they are cut.

Rough material is light in color, but acquires a darker hue during the polishing process. The sandstone cuts quickly on a diamond saw and holds up well while polishing on a flat lap after the loose material is scrubbed away. For whatever reason, polishing the stone on a flat lap brings out a deeper color, though never as rich as Utah sandstone. The once rough surface also gains a glassy sheen. The result from the branching limonite veins is that of a twisted tree branch or landscape.

Plant fossils are most likely Devonian scale trees and scouring rushes and the sandstone itself may be part of the Verango Formation. The plant fossils are usually scaly bark and stems embedded in the sandstone. Most fossils range from one to two inches long. Others are more than a foot long. Larger specimens tend to be on the broken faces of sandstone boulders that make extraction difficult.

Rough picture sandstone and plant fossils.

Highland Picture Sandstone

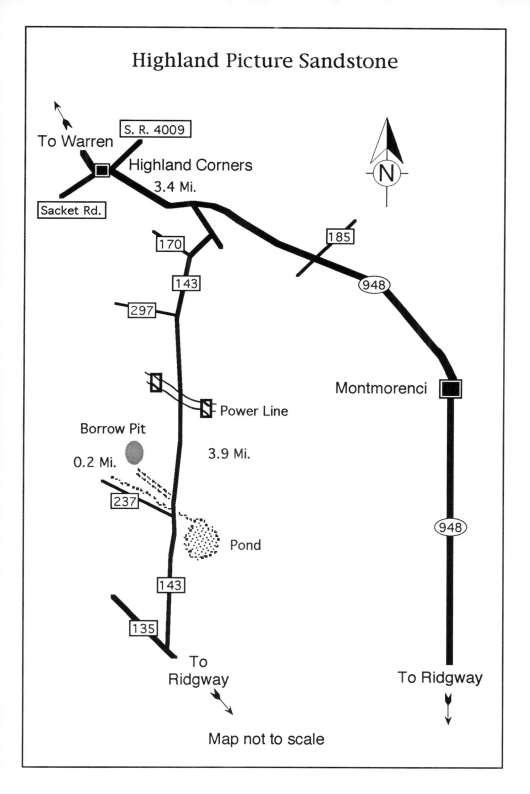

Map not to scale

site 16 LOCK HAVEN RIPPLE MARKS

A Silurian coral reef is exposed along a roadside near the small Pennsylvania town of Castanea. Castanea is across Bald Eagle Creek from the larger town of Lock Haven. Travel 0.8 mile from Castanea on S. R. 2012 and park on the roadside. The tilted coral reef and its rippled surface are clearly visible about 200 yards south of the road. It is worth the effort just to stop and observe this huge reminder of Pennsylvania's warmer past.

The reef, now part of the Mifflintown Formation, formed about 415 million years ago in a tropical sea. Prehistoric corals, just like corals today, form reefs only in the clear, shallow waters of tropical climates. The folding and buckling of the Pennsylvania landscape has since turned the once horizontal reef to a steep angle on the hillside. This fortunate geologic event exposes a wide section of the reef all at once and the position of the angle allows you to look "down" at the reef from a distance.

Ripple marks, formed in sand and mud by wave action millions of years ago, cover parts of the reef. The raised S-like pattern is present in rocks that fall to the base of the reef and on some portions of the dirt road running parallel to the reef. People occasionally deliver similar ripple marks to museums for identification with the mistaken belief that they are "fossil snakes." Although the ripple marks are not colorful, they are large enough to make very interesting display pieces and teaching tools.

Pennsylvania Geologic Survey publications note the presence of fossil colonial corals such as *Favosites* and *Coenites*, bryozoa, brachiopods and ostracods at the reef site. Most of the fossils observed by the authors were not very well preserved. A section of the reef's easternmost part collapsed in a massive landslide (probably after tropical storm Beryl in 1994). The rubble adorns the eastern cliff base. As the mud from this slide weathers away, collectors may find better preserved fossils in the debris and newly exposed reef.

Walk across the field and move along the cliff base to search for ripple marks and fossils. Be very careful if you intend to climb the loose talus slope or onto the reef itself. There is always the danger of falling rocks. The authors also spotted some good quality jasper while examining some nearby construction. The source of the jasper is unknown, but collectors may want to watch for it while exploring the surrounding area.

Lock Haven Ripple Marks

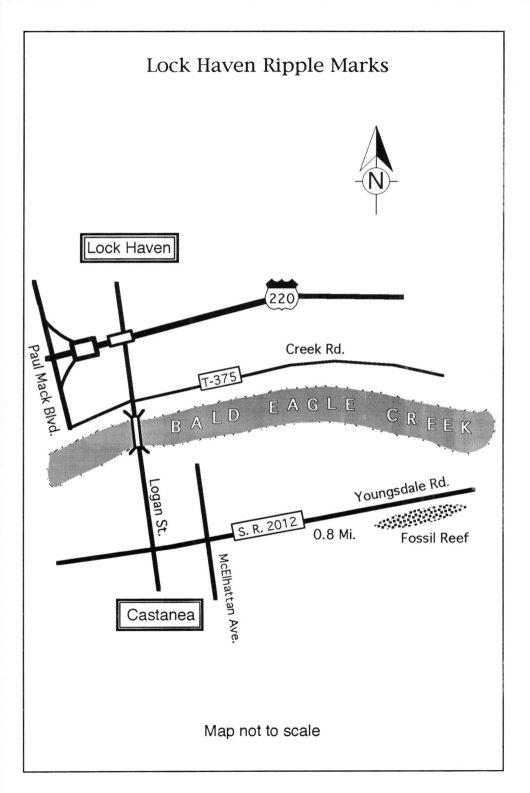

Map not to scale

JERSEY SHORE CALCITE & QUARTZ ———

The town of Jersey Shore, Pennsylvania has one of the most confusing names possible. The town lies west of Williamsport and very far from the New Jersey coastline. Despite the confusing name, mineral collectors visit Jersey Shore because of the abandoned limestone quarries with a treasure of calcite, quartz and strontianite.

Two such quarries remain near the banks of Pine Creek. To reach them follow Main Street south from Jersey Shore (Main Street becomes Tiadaughton Drive). Turn right onto Pine Creek Drive just before the bridge across the creek. Quarry "A" is 0.9 mile down Pine Creek Drive across the street from an auto shop. Since the last edition, "no trespassing" signs have been posted at the quarries. Do not enter without permission. Quarry "B" is 0.2 mile back toward Tiadaughton Drive and 0.1 mile down a dirt road on the north side of the road.

Quarry "A" cuts through Devonian rocks of the Onondaga Formation. The quarry looks uninviting as you walk in because it is overgrown with weeds. Be careful of wood and metal debris, nails and standing water as you move around the quarry. Look toward the wall at the back of the quarry and you will notice an unusual depression or fault in the horizontal limestone layers.

A little searching in the quarry rubble on the side and in the back should quickly reveal some interesting finds of calcite and quartz crystals. Calcite crystals are clear to golden yellow at quarry "A." Look for small, but beautiful double and single-terminated quartz crystals growing on top of limestone or calcite. The mineral strontianite is a rare find at the quarry and appears as small cotton-like tufts in calcite vugs. Some of the upper layers also contain Devonian marine fossils.

Quarry "B" has a pile of rubble at the quarry's rear with larger calcite crystals colored clear to deep orange. The best calcite specimens will probably be found here, though there are fewer quartz crystals. Masses of calcite crystals are in vugs between thin sheets of limestone. It is easiest to look for crystal cavities already partly exposed in the broken rock. Large pieces of gray-black flint are also present in the rubble. This quarry, like the other, contains a great deal of trash and debris from people using it as a dump and target range. Be very careful while walking around or driving your car into this quarry because of nails. Both quarries are swampy with an ample supply of mosquitoes in summer. Conditions in both quarries make these locations inadvisable for young children.

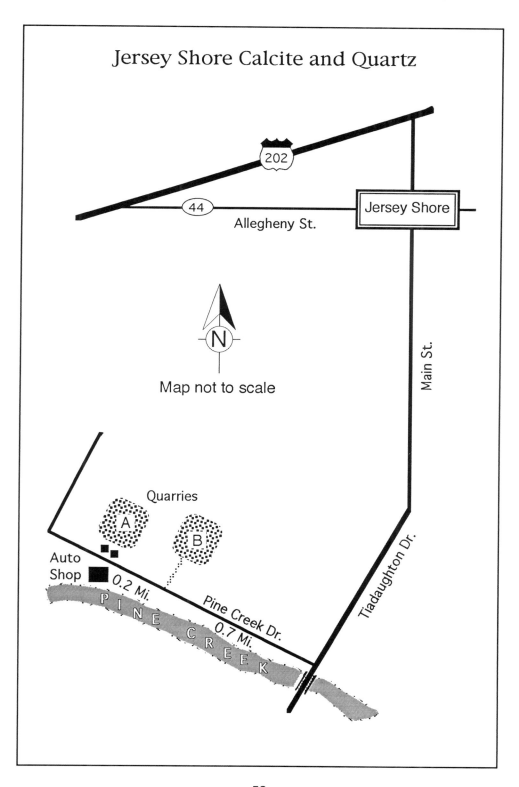

Jersey Shore Calcite and Quartz

Map not to scale

ANTES CREEK FOSSILS

Collectors can sample some of Pennsylvania's fine Ordovician fossils at outcrops near Antes Creek, about 16 miles southwest of Williamsport. To reach the site, take State Highway 654 from Williamsport to its intersection with State Highway 44 near Collomsville. Turn right and continue 0.4 mile to the intersection of State Highway 880 and turn left. Look for a road cut 4.0 miles south of the intersection on the west side of the road. Continue past the road cut and look for a pullover another 0.1 mile down the road on the east side.

The road exposes an outcrop of Ordovician shale at this gap in Bald Eagle Mountain. The Salona Formation shale is a deep slaty gray and contains marine fossils from seas that existed across Pennsylvania more than 425 million years ago. Fossils at the road cut include brachiopods, crinoid columns, bryozoa and trilobites.

Crumbled fossil-bearing shale has fallen by the edge of the road and is the best place to begin your search. Unfortunately, there is almost no shoulder for you to work on. Be careful not to allow rock to fall into the roadway while you work. Collectors must also be constantly aware of the closeness of the road traffic that is heavy at times. As such, it is not a good place to bring children.

Small crinoid stems and brachiopods will probably be among the first fossil finds. A little diligent searching and some splitting of shale with a chisel will yield larger specimens of the broad brachiopod *Dalmanella*. Other brachiopods include *Plectorthis, Sowerbyella* and *Rafinesquina*. Despite their age, brachiopods at Antes Creek are often white with much of their original shell material. Of particular interest to many collectors will be specimens of the ornamented trilobites *Cryptolithus* and *Ceraurus*. Most of the trilobites present at the cut are fragmentary. Relatively complete heads and bodies are fairly common.

As you walk north along the road cut you will see a dense band of broken shell material at about head level or higher. The wall becomes wetter as you go with a subsequent increase in slugs, moss and dripping water. The cut exposes micro-calcite crystals in this vicinity.

Road cuts on State Highway 44 expose Ordovician Reedsville, Antes and Coburn Formations in the Antes Gap area for those looking for additional fossil collecting. Look for shale exposures about 0.5 mile in either direction of the intersection with State Highway 880.

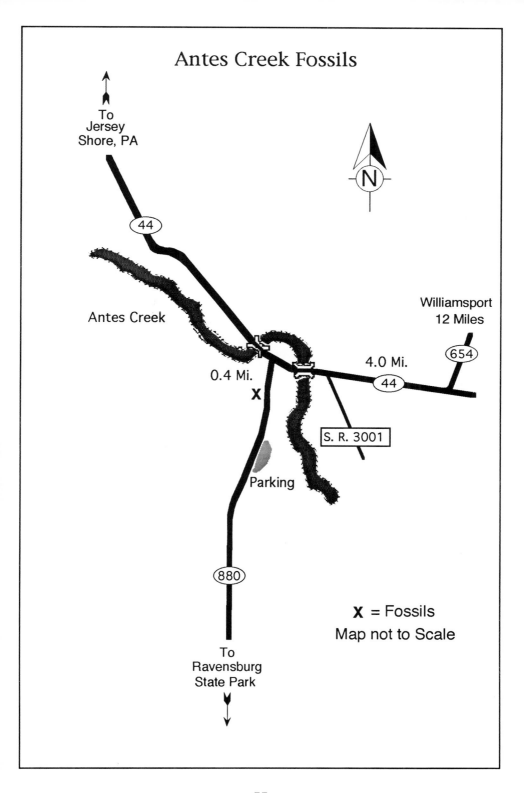

Antes Creek Fossils

To Jersey Shore, PA

44

Antes Creek

N

Williamsport 12 Miles

654

0.4 Mi.

X

4.0 Mi.

44

S. R. 3001

Parking

880

To Ravensburg State Park

X = Fossils
Map not to Scale

RALSTON FOSSIL LEAVES

A collecting site for exquisite fossil leaves is situated near the tiny village of Ralston, roughly 25 miles north of Williamsport, Pennsylvania on State Highway 14. Ralston is just beyond the State Highway 14 bridge over Lycoming Creek when traveling from the south. Pass by a small road that crosses the stream to a residential area and turn east at an unmarked road in the center of town. There is a bridge across Lycoming Creek in 0.2 mile.

The road will quickly become a dirt road after the bridge as it heads up onto the mountain. The unpaved road divides in 0.5 mile into McIntyre Road heading left and Rock Run Road heading right. Count yourself lucky if you can find a sign. Follow McIntyre Road another 2.5 miles to the abandoned strip mine on the right side of the road across from the overgrown clearings of a town long gone.

A small trail leads from the road to a low pile of shale debris that marks the mine's location. Walk to the other side of the pile and look for pieces of red-black shale or mudstone in the old mine dumps surrounding a swampy depression. The mine dumps are not obvious and at first appear to be only a weedy hillside. Look through the layer of living plants and wildflowers to see bits of shale scattered on the ground. Search the flat area behind the debris pile and the slopes leading down into the depression for fossils exposed by erosion. You will probably find more fossils by looking for rocks exposed by weather than by digging. A little tapping with a rock hammer or prying with a screw driver may help locate fossils in larger pieces of rock.

The fossil leaves belong to seed ferns of the genus *Neuropteris*. Seed ferns dominated Pennsylvanian coal swamps and were the first plants to develop true seeds rather than spores. *Neuropteris* fossils at McIntyre are usually a single, narrow leaf one to two inches long. Rocks at the site may have more than one leaf fossil, but are rarely connected by a stem as is often the case with fern fossils. Delicate veins and textures are finely preserved in the leaves and easily visible. The leaf fossils are slightly raised from the surface of the broken shale giving them an embossed appearance on the rock. *Neuropteris* is only one of several dozen genus of seed ferns. Other types of fern fossils may certainly be present at the site.

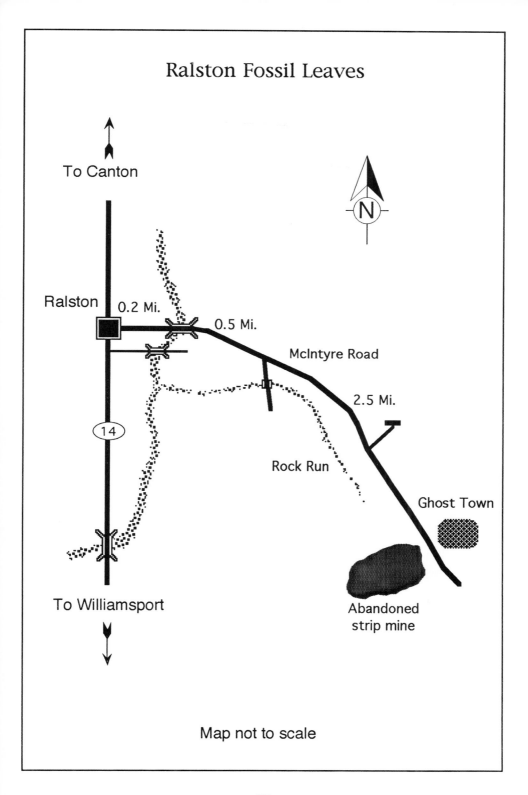

Ralston Fossil Leaves

To Canton

N

Ralston   0.2 Mi.

0.5 Mi.

McIntyre Road

14

2.5 Mi.

Rock Run

Ghost Town

To Williamsport

Abandoned
strip mine

Map not to scale

New rock exposed after a landslide near the Pennsylvania town of Lock Haven.

One of the collecting sites at Jersey Shore — quarry "A."

Broken shale along the roadway in outcrops near Antes Creek.

A typical fossil found along McIntyre Road near Ralston.

WILLIAMSPORT AMMONITES

The difficulties of collecting rocks and minerals in the eastern United States are many. Most of the challenges in finding suitable collecting localities are summed up in one word: rain. The humid environment means lush vegetation, and ground cover means a lack of exposed rock. For the collector, it requires learning to look at every borrow pit and road cut encountered. A look at all the exposed rocks in an area might bring a discovery that will make your day.

On the west side of Williamsport, PA is a borrow pit that gives new meaning to serendipity. Looking initially like an adequate source of limonite-stained sandstone, it quickly yielded fossil crinoid stems, ripple marks, dendritic swirls on shale—and ammonoids. There is something here for almost every interest, collectible in a short time.

The survival of this site is problematic. Enter the borrow pit only if it is not posted. Unfortunately, the access of many borrow pits and quarries changes frequently. Be alert for other recent excavations in the area that may expose the same fossil layer or others.

Access is from High Street, a little west of the light at Oliver and High Streets. Park at the first level spot on the south side of the pit. This is a big borrow pit, so plan for much walking. To find the greatest variety of minerals and fossils, you must climb several levels of the pit and keep your eyes open for possibilities.

Swirls of color attract the eye first. Look for orange, red, and brown stains of limonite on coarse-grained sandstone. Some pieces are small enough for cutting good examples of picture rock. Dendritic swirls of manganese create miniature landscapes and underwater scenes on dark gray shale, which are just the right size for small vertical displays.

The ripple marks of the Devonian sea floor are appealing. It is impressive to stand where once there was an ancient sea, alive with creatures that live in our imaginations. Photos of the ripple marks are the easiest way to bring home these treasures.

There are also fossils. Crinoid, or sea-lily, stems are common but not large. The ammonoids are more subtle, blending into the host rock. Most of the ammonoids are 3" in diameter, though they range in size from one to four inches. Once they make themselves known, it's easy to find them by looking at dark red layers of fallen rock. It's more difficult to extract them from the boulders, so look for smaller rocks.

The shales can be split with a screwdriver, not even requiring a hammer. Bring plenty of water for your walk for it is like any open quarry with no shade. Wearing boots and jeans will keep the rough edges of shale away from your skin. Bring a camera for a record of the colorful or interesting large pieces. Many of them will shatter if you attempt to knock them off the host rock.

Williamsport Ammonites

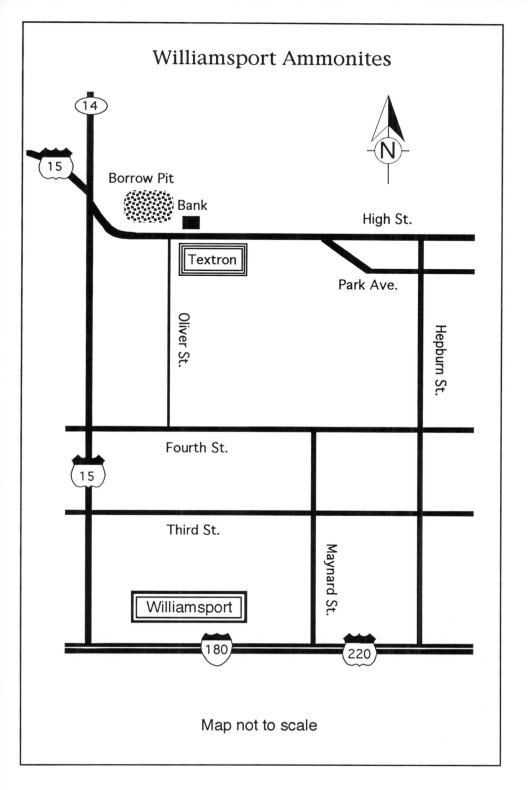

Map not to scale

CRYSTAL POINT DIAMOND MINE ―――――

The abundance of quartz crystals at the Crystal Point Diamond Mine outside Williamsport, Pennsylvania rivals that of many distant locations. Crystalline seams hidden in the wooded slopes above the Susquehanna River hold untold tons of glittering quartz crystals. The mine's owner, Ray Smith, leads collectors by prior arrangement to the mine from Raytowne in Williamsport.

Raytowne is a recently converted brick factory-warehouse now housing a country dance club, restaurant, and shops. To get to Raytowne take U.S. Highway 15 north from Interstate 180 and enter Williamsport on High Street. Bear right onto Park Avenue and look for the large brick buildings of Raytowne on the right just past Cemetery Street. The chimney at Raytowne sports a large "R."

After meeting at Raytowne, collectors need to follow Mr. Smith a few miles in their car to get to the mine site. The last leg of the trip is down a rough jeep trail and a high clearance vehicle or a lift from Mr. Smith will be necessary.

The mine and surrounding land is part of an area where Smith hunted as a youngster. He started to find crystals on a heavily used deer trail and started digging by hand until he found the quartz vein. Now with the benefit of heavy machinery, he can dig along the side of the vein without breaking much of the material. Loose crystals, clusters weighing up to 15 or 20 pounds, and many aggregates of 50-60 pounds are common. Smith has seen pieces that probably weigh a ton or two.

The Crystal Point Diamond Mine is really a long cut, about 200 yards long and 12 feet deep, dug into the side of Bald Eagle Mountain. The steep walls of the trench can be difficult to navigate especially if it is muddy. Wet weather has its benefits, however, because the red clay is soft for digging. Finding the crystals is not a problem. Quartz crystals lay scattered everywhere along the trench and are piled up on the sides. Trying to pick out which crystals you want is the challenge.

Digging for fresh crystals is a delicate matter because picks and shovels easily damage them. The best tool to probe the red clay for quartz, a least when the ground is soft, is a small garden claw. The mine owner will show you the best places to start and you will not need to dig far. Each scraping of the claw reveals quartz crystals of all sizes if you dig right at the seam. Bring other small tools like hammers, shovels and screw drivers (The right tool for the right job!) according to your taste. Work gloves will save your hands from the extremely sharp edges of the crystals. A squirt bottle helps to clean

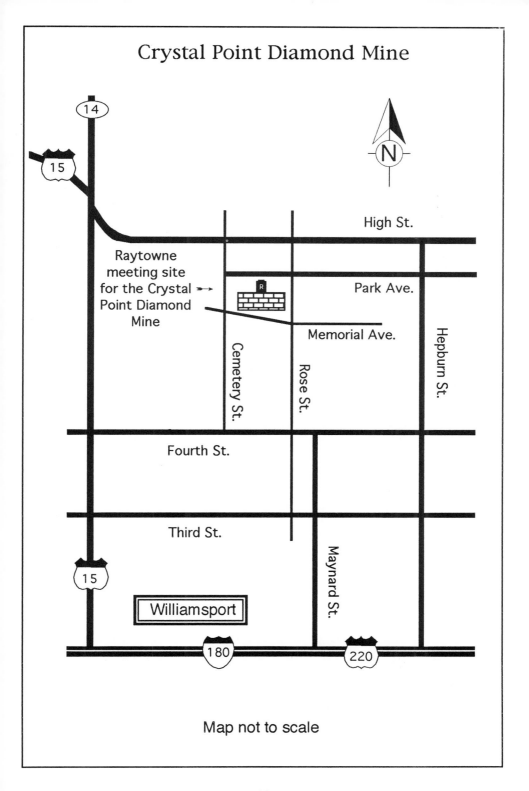

Crystal Point Diamond Mine

Raytowne meeting site for the Crystal Point Diamond Mine

High St.

Park Ave.

Memorial Ave.

Cemetery St.

Rose St.

Hepburn St.

Fourth St.

Third St.

Maynard St.

Williamsport

14

15

15

180

220

Map not to scale

the crystals before you pack your bucket(s). Wrap the quartz in newspaper or other packing material to protect the crystals from damaging each other during travel.

Quartz crystals at Crystal Point are often wide and impressively sized single terminations, clusters or aggregates. The crystals usually have a yellow or amber appearance due to a rusty iron stain. Soaking the quartz in oxalic acid for a day to a week after a thorough scrubbing with water removes the coating (Oxalic acid is available in many hardware stores). It's not too hard to find pieces of strawberry quartz (crystals sprinkled with red dots of hematite), black to light smoky quartz and citrine.

The fee of $30 per person allows collectors ten pounds of crystals. Additional crystals can be purchased back at Raytowne. To contact the mine write: Crystal Point Diamond Mine, c/o Raytowne, 1307 Park Avenue, Williamsport, PA 17701 or call (570) 323-6783.

The trench of the Crystal Point Diamond Mine.

MONTOUR FOSSIL PIT _____

There are many outcrops of Middle Devonian fossils in Pennsylvania. The most user-friendly of all is located at the Montour Preserve just north of Washingtonville. The Montour Preserve is a 966-acre nature and recreation preserve owned by the Pennsylvania Power & Light Company and the fossil pit on the property is open from sunrise to sunset.

To reach the pit, turn east from Route 54 onto S. R. 1006 and travel 2.6 miles to the preserve headquarters. The pit is another 1.4 miles down the road on the right across from eastern end of Lake Chillisquaque. Restrooms and picnic facilities are located near the lake shore as you travel to the collecting area. A sign and well-groomed parking area marks the entrance to the pit. The fossil site is a short walk from the parking area and clearly marked by a large poster sign with pictures of the fossils that are present. The Montour Pit really is the most genial collecting site you are likely to encounter.

The word pit does not describe the location very well since you begin at the bottom and look up at it. The pit appears more like a long talus slope of shale and tilted bedding. The dark gray to tan shale and mudstone is an outcrop of the Mahantango Formation deposited in a shallow Devonian sea about 385 million years ago. Mudstone layers are primarily horizontal and show little folding and faulting in this area. Material was excavated from the pit for use as fill exposing the fossils.

Fossils at the pit are not abundant in every layer. It may take some trial and error to locate a good spot to work. The fastest way to locate fossil bearing layers is to search around where others have already been digging. Use a small shovel, rock hammer, sharp chisel, awl or screwdriver and wear safety glasses to remove layers for splitting. Shale at the pit is incredibly brittle and collectors will need to use special care to remove specimens intact. Paper and aluminum foil wrapping will be helpful in keeping specimens safe during the trip home. The most common fossils here include brachiopods, bryozoa, crinoids, coral, coelenterates, cephalopods and pelecypods. Trilobites such as *Phacops* and *Greenops* are also common in the Mahantango Formation. Concretions at the site sometimes contain siderite, chalcopyrite or malachite stain.

Additional information is available at the Preserve Visitor Center, open year-round Monday through Friday 9 a.m. to 4 p.m. and weekends 12 p.m. to 4 p.m. from May through September. You can contact the Montour Preserve by writing PP&L Montour Preserve, 700 Preserve Road, Danville, PA 17821 or calling (570) 437-3131.

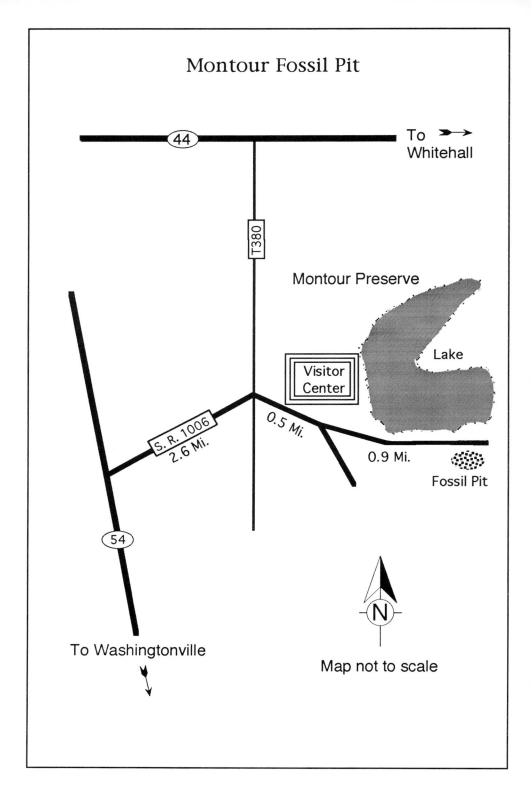

Montour Fossil Pit

To → Whitehall

44

T380

Montour Preserve

Visitor Center

Lake

S. R. 1006
2.6 Mi.

0.5 Mi.

0.9 Mi.

Fossil Pit

54

To Washingtonville

N

Map not to scale

EASTERN INDUSTRIES QUARRY

Some of Pennsylvania's finest and most colorful calcite crystals come from the Winfield limestone quarry. Collector-friendly quarries are always a breath of fresh air, especially in the East, and once a year the Eastern Industries Quarry at Winfield opens its gate to the public. The quarry's open house is usually on the third Saturday in September, but times and dates can vary. Checking with the quarry in advance is certainly recommended. The pleasant atmosphere of the event is a real plus for the Winfield Quarry. Refreshments are often sold by the local high school band boosters. Tailgate dealers offer collectors a few extra mineral possibilities to peruse while resting up from working the pit. Pickup trucks transport collectors to and from the quarry floor. The event helped the quarry win a Gold Medallion Award from the National Stone Association in Washington.

Winfield Quarry is a massive rectangular quarry that cuts 80 to 150 feet down into the Old Port, Keyser and Tonoloway Formations of Silurian and Devonian Age. The Keyser Formation is the quarry's main commercial objective. The mineralized seam of the Tonoloway Formation about 20 to 30 feet below the Keyser attracts mineral collector's interest. The seam is the source for spectacular clear, golden and iridescent calcite crystals common in the quarry. Calcite crystals at the quarry get their iridescence from a thin limonite coating. Massive calcite also abounds at the quarry.

Other common minerals include strontianite, quartz, fluorite and pink dolomite. The strontianite seems most abundant in vugs found in the rocks of the eastern wall. A greater variety of minerals was once found in the older part of the quarry that is now back filled, but there is still the possibility of encountering minerals like celestite, galena, pyrite and others. Fossil collectors should ask about the fossiliferous shale layers in the upper portions of the quarry. Coral, brachiopods and crinoid stems are common in some of the shale layers.

Collectors visiting the quarry on open house day must have a hard hat, safety shoes and wear safety glasses when hammering. Visitors must sign a liability release form and pay a nominal registration fee before entering the quarry. In addition to the usual backpack, bucket, chisels and newspaper, a heavy rock hammer is useful at the quarry because many of the best specimens are on the faces of large limestone boulders. A four-pound crack hammer can reduce the work time from hours to minutes for some specimens. There is a great deal of clay at the contact zone between the Keyser and Tonoloway Formations. Working at the quarry is a muddy experience, especially if it rains. It almost always does on open house day so you may wish to bring a change of clothes and extra shoes.

Eastern Industries' Winfield Quarry is located just outside the town of Winfield on Amish Road. Travel State Highway 304 from U.S. Highway 15 for a distance of 0.1 mile and follow the road as it turns right. Travel on State Highway 304 another 1.2 miles and turn left onto Amish Road. The quarry entrance is located 0.5 mile farther on the right. Signs usually mark the meeting location on open house day, but you should check with the quarry in advance to be sure. The best time to contact the quarry for information is around May. If you are part of a club, please have one person get on the mailing list for the whole club and distribute copies of the information for members. Keeping the mailing list down to a reasonable size helps the quarry in their open house efforts. To contact the quarry write: Eastern Industries, Inc., P.O. Box 177, Winfield, PA 17889-0177.

Never attempt to enter the quarry on any day other than open house.

Limestone exposures on the quarry wall.

Eastern Industries Quarry

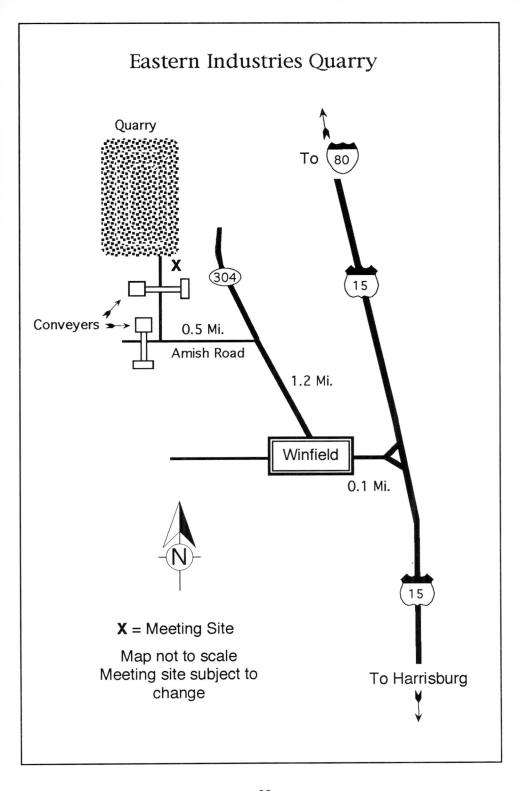

Quarry

X

(304)

Conveyers

0.5 Mi.

Amish Road

1.2 Mi.

To (80)

(15)

Winfield

0.1 Mi.

(15)

To Harrisburg

N

X = Meeting Site

Map not to scale
Meeting site subject to
change

CARBONDALE FOSSIL FERNS _____

Plant fossils are plentiful in the coal-bearing rock of Pennsylvania. During the Pennsylvanian period, about 300 million years ago, trees and ferns grew in the swamps that covered large portions of what is now the Commonwealth. Plants fell below the water surface of the ancient swamps when they died and sediments covered and preserved them before they could decay. Lack of oxygen preserves the soft tissues of plants for fossilization.

All spoil piles from coal strip mining are considered fair game for a plant fossil search. Just find ones that do not say "no trespassing." As more mines are reclaimed, it is a pleasure to find dumps to search.

Access to the dumps near the Carbondale High School is not as easy as it once was, but the fossil rushes make it worth the effort. The rushes belong to the genus *Calamites*, which grew to heights of 50 feet. These tree-like plants had hollow stems and conspicuous joints. Today's horsetail rushes are the sole survivors of the class Sphenopsida, to which the *Calamites* belong. A small rush that grew with the giant *Calamites* and belongs to the same class is *Sphenophyllum*. Stems of *Calamites* and *Sphenophyllum* are good finds in this location.

Take U.S. Highway 6 from Interstate 81 to get to the site, and on your way, stop by Archbald Pothole State Park to look at Pennsylvania's largest glacial pothole. Continue on U.S. Highway 6 past the junction with State Highway 107. Three miles past the junction is a road to Carbondale Elementary and High School parking lots on the west side of the road. There are a few shops on the left before the school, behind which you can park if you would like to climb the piles of shale the hard way.

An easier way is to go another 0.3 mile to an unmarked road leading to an apartment complex. Turn left and travel 0.1 mile to the apartments. From the entrance, drive 0.2 mile into the complex to a partially paved road on the right. Take this road to the rear of the apartments and in 0.1 mile turn left onto the dirt road. At the end of this road, park and walk through the woods to another dirt road. This dirt road is the continuation of the road to the school parking lots you passed on U.S. Highway 6. The most productive piles are here. You will want to check out the other shale piles for potential fossil finds. Do not stray into areas posted by a local gun club.

Use caution when climbing the piles of rock. The shale is slippery, especially after or during a rainfall. A hammer and chisel are useful in

Carbondale Fossil Ferns

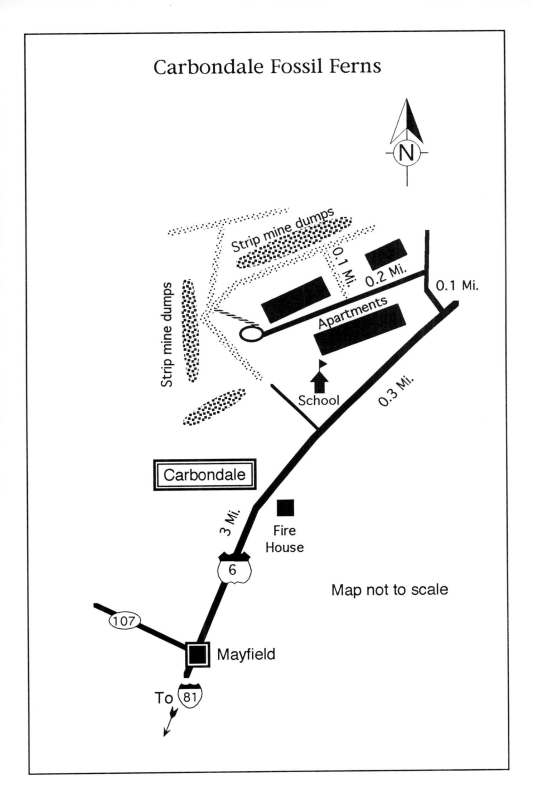

splitting some rock, but walking around in that stooping way rockhounds develop and turning over rocks is just as efficient. Wrapping paper is essential for any plant fossils. The rock is brittle and protection will keep the fossils in one piece.

Some exceptional specimens from the strip mine dumps in Carbondale.

DEER LAKE BRACHIOPODS

An excellent site for a variety of Devonian mollusks is an abandoned borrow pit in Deer Lake, Pennsylvania. Brachiopods and pelecypods are abundant in the Mahantango Formation of the Middle Devonian. There are more than a dozen genera present according to a Pennsylvania State Geological Survey publication. The trilobite genus *Trimerus* is common at the borrow pit, with additional genera of trilobites reported from other shale pits in the area. Gastropods and cephalopods are also more common in the other pits.

The rock strata exposed in the pit are gray, silty shales. Layers of mud accumulated on the sea bottom 380 million years ago and provided habitat for a number of burrowing organisms such as pelecypods. The feeding burrows of *Zoophycops*, a soft worm-like creature, are also abundant. The fossils of all these burrowing organisms are found as orange-stained molds.

To reach this easy roadside location, take State Highway 61 west toward Deer Lake. State Highway 895 East enters State Highway 61 from the right in Molino. Look for 895 West veering left from State Highway 61 a little to the north, but stay on State Highway 61. You are now in Deer Lake, and in about 200 feet, the pit will be on the left side of the road. If you reach the cemetery, you have gone too far.

The front of the pit is in use as a parking area for trucks, so park toward the sides of the pit, out of the way. Watch for broken glass and other debris while parking and while collecting. Collecting the fossils could not be easier. Hammering the shale is not always necessary, especially after or during rain. Simple splitting is almost all that is required to find some good specimens of *Mucrospirifer, Chonetes* and *Orbiculoidea* brachiopods. Collecting at the back, or southern end of the pit is most productive. The mussels or clams you find may include *Leptodesma, Paleoneilo, Leiopteria,* and *Grammysioidea.* Since there is no hard rock mining involved, this is a good place to bring children. Make sure they are watchful of the broken glass and stay away from the parked trucks.

It is a good idea to check out other construction sites, road cuts, and borrow pits in this area for similar collecting sites. New ones are always possible. Ask permission of private property owners and observe all "no trespassing" signs.

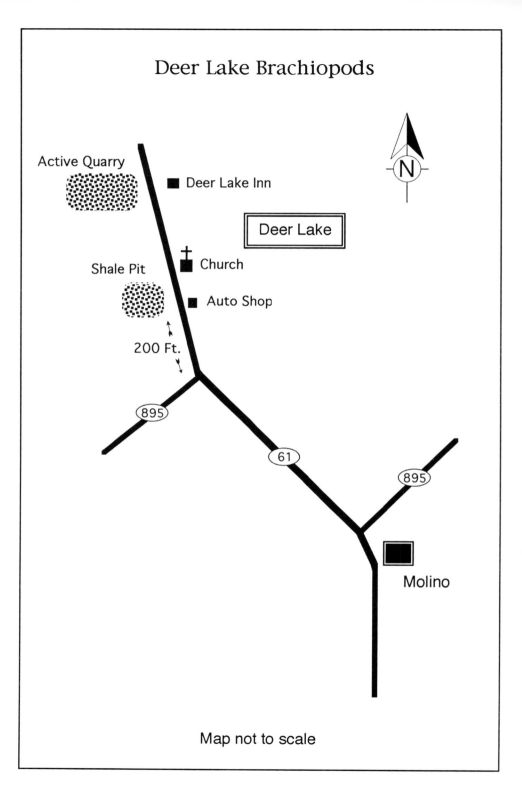

Deer Lake Brachiopods

MORGANTOWN MINERALS _____

A huge magnetite ore body extends deep beneath southeastern Pennsylvania. Mine dumps in the Morgantown area expose minerals from the ore body, but once extensive mine spoils are being crushed and carried away along with the mineral treasure within them.

The mine spoils are from the Grace Magnetite Mine that ceased production in 1976. The mine delved to a depth of 1500 to 3600 feet to recover as much as 11 million tons of the magnetite ore. The mine's current owners, Independence Construction Materials, crush the rock for use as aggregate in road building material. The mine dumps are off limits to collecting unless arrangements are made with the Aggregate Sales Manager of Independence Construction Materials.

Mineview Drive is reached from State Highway 10, north from State Highway 23 in Morgantown, and 0.2 miles north of the entrance to Interstate Highway 76. The distance to the mine office on Mineview Drive is 0.5 mile. The road continues as a landfill road, for which there is no outlet, so you must watch for large, fast-moving trucks.

At the time of publication, the company was exploring the best way to handle mine tours and collecting opportunities in the mine dumps. The Philadelphia Mineralogical Society, a member of the Eastern Federation of Mineralogical Clubs and Lapidary Societies, is in contact with the company for possible trips. The society organizes and supervises field trips, open to members of other clubs with a valid membership card from an EFMLS club. DO NOT attempt to enter the mine on your own, or collecting opportunities may be denied to everyone.

Each person must bring a hard hat, safety shoes, and safety glasses and sign a liability release. Bring a rock hammer, bucket, and gloves for your collecting trip. The brittle serpentine rock fractures in unexpected ways. Whichever way the rock breaks, it is almost always sharp.

About 30 minerals are present at the Morgantown site. Collectors may quickly spot magnetite, actinolite, pyrite, chalcopyrite, chlorite, natrolite, hematite, calcite, phlogopite, and biotite. The rocks of the mine consist of serpentine, limestone, and metamorphic mixtures. The cutting

A portion of the mine dump still remains.

and lapidary potential of the rocks seem endless. Green swirls and intriguing lines fill the serpentine stones.

In just three years, mine dumps in an industrial center overlooking the mine disappeared, along with the "grace" name honoring the mine. The future of the remaining mine dumps is limited, but access to them is possible through the good graces of the new mine owners.

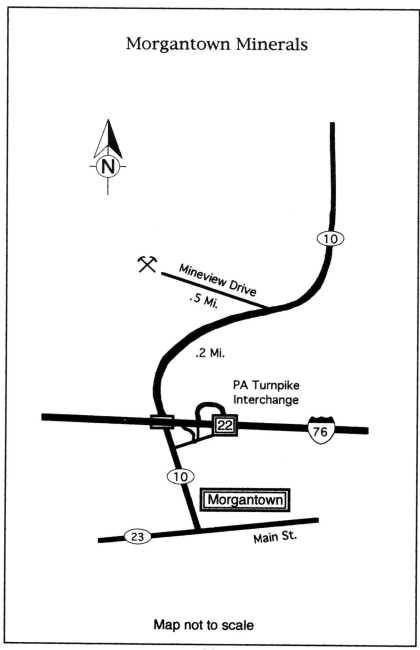

Morgantown Minerals

Map not to scale

Collectors gathered striking red and yellow jasper from the Vera Cruz area outside Allentown for thousands of years. Of course, their motives for collecting were a little different from today's collectors and Allentown is a relatively recent addition to the Pennsylvania landscape. The very first collectors were Paleo Indian people who quarried the area some 14,000 years ago. Native Americans such as the Unami (a name meaning turtle) of the Delaware Indians continued to quarry Vera Cruz jasper until about the 1600s when European metal forging technology replaced Indian stone work.

Prior to this, Native Americans traded the jasper throughout Pennsylvania, New Jersey and beyond. The location of Vera Cruz at a natural gap in the surrounding hills facilitated the trade. Traffic through the convenient gap is also responsible for positioning of the current day Fisher's Tavern at Vera Cruz, constructed in 1754 at the intersection of Main Road and Vera Cruz Road.

The original Indian quarries are now protected as a National Historic Landmark called Jasper Park not far from the tavern on Vera Cruz Road, also know as S. R. 2027. Take time to walk some of the trails to the old Indian quarries at Jasper Park. The trails wind around many pits dug by Native Americans seeking jasper. You can see large blocks of jasper near the parking area and evidence of much more near the quarries. Collecting is not allowed within the park! Please respect the cultural and historic resources that the park protects.

Although the park protects the historically valuable quarries, jasper still abounds throughout the countryside. Most of the surrounding farmland is private property and should not be entered without permission. Any exposed area or stream side near Vera Cruz, however, can produce jasper. A black stain often coats area jasper and masks its color, but a quick inspection will reveal hefty cutting pieces or smaller jasper for tumbling. Some of the jasper has aggregates of tiny quartz crystals on the surface. Please respect property rights and always get permission to collect on private land to insure that collectors can sample Vera Cruz Jasper in the future. If you plan to ask permission to collect in area farm fields, it is best to plan your visits for times of the year that crops are not present in the field. An empty field may make farmers a bit more willing to let you walk around on their land.

Since you are in the neighborhood, it might be a good idea to stop in at the tavern. Tavern owner Dennis Thomasik is something of an enthusiastic history buff and happily spins out all manner of local history while dishing out some tasty Tex/Mex food. Thomasik also keeps local history information binders for his patrons to peruse and will show off some Indian artifacts made from the local jasper.

Take time to walk some of the trails to the old Indian quarries at Jasper Park. The trails wind around many pits dug by Native Americans seeking jasper. You can see large blocks of jasper near the parking area and evidence of much more near the quarries. Collecting, however, is not allowed within the park.

NOTICE! The recent addition of "no parking" signs on S.R. 2027, even on the bridge over Fetterman's Creek, indicates special care must be taken by collectors to respect property owners' rights. There is parking on S.R. 2027, south of the intersection with S.R. 2023.

Typical jasper specimens from the stream.

Vera Cruz Jasper

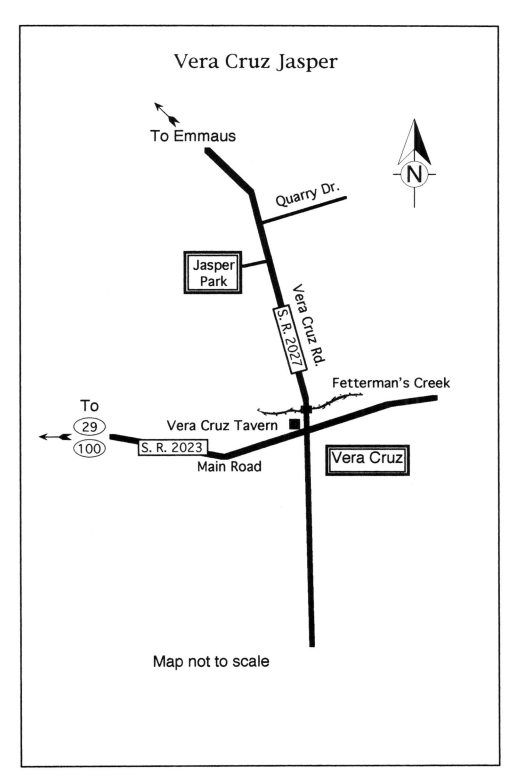

Map not to scale

HELLERTOWN JASPER & QUARTZ

The region surrounding Allentown, Pennsylvania is rich with colorful jasper. An easy way to collect some cutting material is to rummage around in the waters of Silver Creek. Silver Creek winds through Hellertown, south of Allentown, and empties into Saucon Creek on its way to the Lehigh River. Jasper and small weathered quartz crystals are present along the entire length of Silver Creek, though a large section of the stream passes through a private golf course.

Anywhere that you can poke around the stream bank is likely to net you some jasper. There is a parking area across the street from Lost River Caverns that is a good place to start. To reach the parking area, travel south 1.2 miles from Interstate 78 on State Highway 412 in Hellertown. Turn left onto Penn Street (quickly becoming Durham Street) and drive 0.5 mile to the cavern. The parking area, belonging to the cavern owners, is on the left across from the cavern. The many signs directing you to the cavern will help you find your way.

Stream waters pour across a few jasper boulders that are a bit too large for a backpack so search stream banks and gravel bars for smaller pieces. In warm weather, we recommend walking right in to look for the shiny quartz. There is a large gravel bar beneath a covered bridge that produced a keeper for the authors. A rare, but exciting find in the creek are nodules of the manganese mineral beraunite. Jasper in the stream is often the yellow-orange variety, but also includes blue-gray jasper with an almost flinty appearance.

A large polished piece of exceptional local flint is on display with many other minerals inside the combination museum and gift shop at Lost River Caverns. The building's back wall, now home to a collection of tropical plants, is actually the rear wall of an old limestone quarry. Work at the quarry may be responsible for the quartz crystals in Silver Creek. Limestone of the Leithsville formation was used as flux in the production of iron ore from the nearby Bachman Iron Mine (now defunct). Quarry work also broke into the first of five chambers that make up the cavern. A rock and lapidary supply shop is also at the cavern entrance.

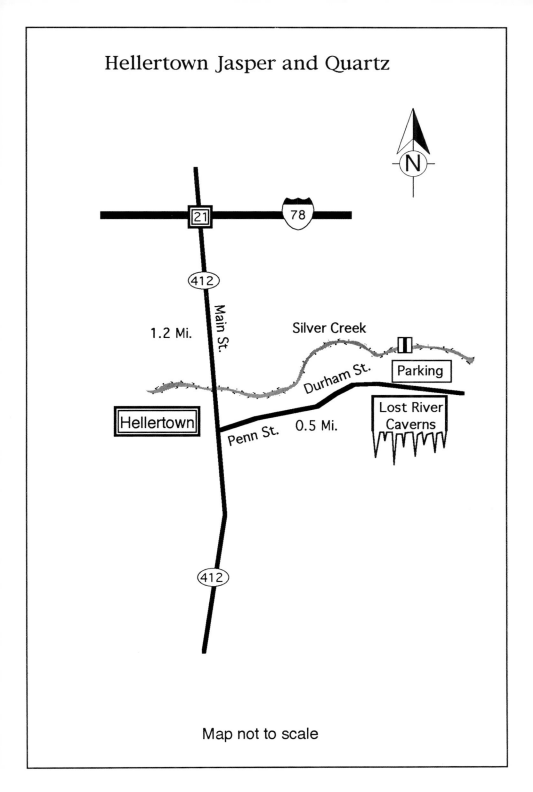

Hellertown Jasper and Quartz

N

21 78

412

1.2 Mi.

Main St.

Silver Creek

Durham St.

Parking

Hellertown

Penn St.   0.5 Mi.

Lost River
Caverns

412

Map not to scale

Collecting jasper beneath the covered bridge at Silver Creek outside of Hellertown.

Working part of the old quarry wall for Eastonite.

The lure of a mineral from its type locality can lead the intrepid collector to a badly overgrown quarry. The collector does not even mind if the quarry is next to an extremely busy road, where a necessary tool is a leaf rake. Never mind that the mineral in question, eastonite, is a questionable mineral at best. Eastonite was previously depicted as a variety of phlogopite, but more recent tests show that the material is a submicroscopic mixture of phlogopite and serpentine. Eastonite occurs in a lovely shade of green.

North of the city of Easton, Pennsylvania, on the southeast side of Chestnut Hill, Forks Township is a wide spot by the side of State Highway 611. That wide spot was once a quarry, overlooking the Delaware River, now currently used for fun by rock climbers.

State Highway 611 North from U.S. Highway 22 is not fun. From New Jersey, State Highway 611 is the first unexpected turn from the bridge. From U.S. Highway 22 in Pennsylvania, getting to 611 North requires following the signs meticulously. At 1.1 miles north of U.S. Highway 22, you will pass the water treatment plant on the river side of the road. Start looking for an Easton Water Bureau building on the same side in about 0.2 mile.

A gravel area just north of this structure provides parking for a couple of vehicles. Two additional parking areas are possible, 0.3 and 1.1 miles north of the first. The second parking area is a scenic overlook on the Delaware River. Do not attempt to park anywhere else along State Highway 611. It is a busy road, with no shoulders and no parking permitted. The quarry in the trees and bushes is opposite the Water Bureau building. Please be considerate for future collectors and do not park in the yard or driveway of the house next to the site.

The best time to visit here is winter or early spring because of the heavy plant growth. There are several pathways leading from the road to the old quarry wall. You will need boots, gloves, a heavy hammer and something to scrape away fallen leaves. An easy method of collecting is to search under the leaves for rocks that have weathered out and tumbled down to the lowest level. The southern end of the hollow proved most productive during a recent visit.

The serpentine-phlogopite mix is common, its micaceous green flakes most evident on the weathered rock. The serpentine group representatives are massive green blocks, a complex mix of lizardite and antigorite species. Talc, calcite, tremolite, and tourmaline group minerals are easy to find. Look for graphite in the Franklin marble, originally of Precambrian origin. Later hydrothermal solutions altered the serpentine group minerals and introduced uranium and thorium minerals.

Eastonite

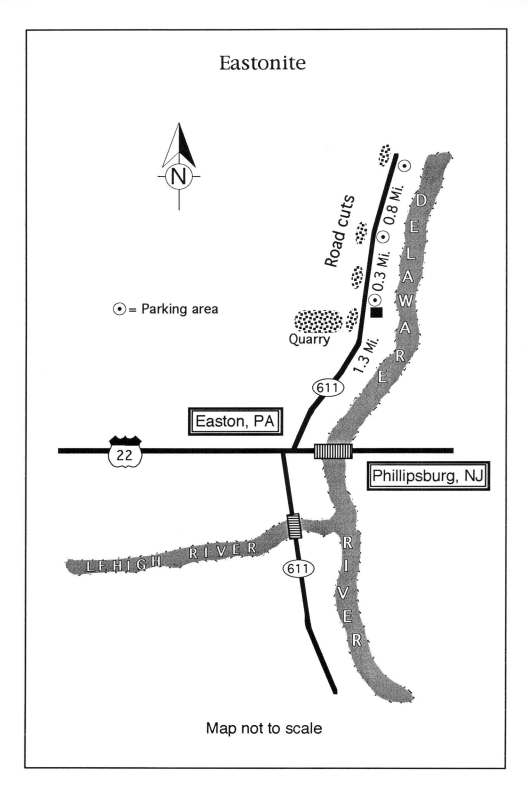

RINGING ROCKS PARK

Although not a collecting site, Ringing Rocks Park permits an attractive and socially responsible outlet for that imperative desire of all rockhounds to pound a rock hammer on a boulder. The payoff here is a pleasant musical sound like the ringing of a bell. Ringing Rocks Park is a Bucks County park located off State Highway 32 just north of the bridge across the Delaware River between Milford, New Jersey and Upper Black Eddy, Pennsylvania. From State Highway 32 north on the Pennsylvania side, turn left onto Bridgeton Hill Road (a steep incline in spots) and travel 1.5 miles. Turn right onto Ringing Rock Road and drive 0.2 mile to the park entrance. A 0.25 mile trail leading to the boulders connects to the back end of the parking area.

Visitors can walk among the rocks gently bashing boulders to find the sound most pleasing to their ear. The clear musical tone, or cacophony depending on the number of people participating, varies distinctly for each rock. Not all the rocks at Ringing Rocks will ring. Many will give a dull "thunk" just the way you would expect them to because of a firm grounding. The rocks with the best tones are perched atop several others with minimal contact. Minimal contact with ground or surrounding rock helps the rock to resonate. Trial and error is the best way to explore Ringing Rocks. Bowl-like depressions on the boulders from years of rock hammer strikes indicate the better ringers. A raised and particularly well pummeled rock near the center of the field may be the champion ringer. Pick your way carefully through the rocks as many of them are uneven or will move when stepped on.

Mechanical erosion exposes the boulders at Ringing Rocks rather than any exotic process or glacial origin. Water carries soil and loose debris from the field and keeps the boulders exposed. The boulders at Ringing Rocks are part of an intrusive diabase mass. According to Pennsylvania state publications, the diabase itself is mostly composed of labradorite feldspar (without the iridescent colors of gem labradorite) and augite (a pyroxene mineral containing elements like calcium, magnesium, iron and alumina). The crystal arrangement within the rock facilitates sound transmission or, in other words, the rock rings when you hit it.

The Ringing Rocks Boulder Field is purportedly the largest such ringing boulder field in the East. We can only speculate on the number of boulder fields actually checked in this fashion. Walking the boulder field and "playing" the rocks is a strange and magical experience. Collectors will not return from Ringing Rocks with specimens, but they will return with a colorful memory and a good story that is in many ways just as profitable.

Ringing Rocks Park

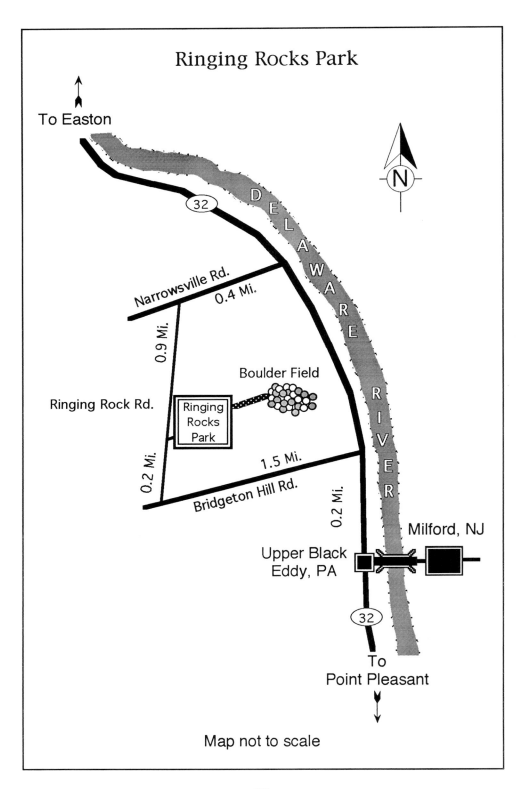

To Easton

32

DELAWARE RIVER

N

Narrowsville Rd.

0.4 Mi.

0.9 Mi.

Boulder Field

Ringing Rock Rd.

Ringing Rocks Park

0.2 Mi.

1.5 Mi.

Bridgeton Hill Rd.

0.2 Mi.

Milford, NJ

Upper Black Eddy, PA

32

To Point Pleasant

Map not to scale

Searching for the right sound at Ringing Rocks Park.

Garnet schist outcrops in the Wissahickon Valley.

WISSAHICKON VALLEY GARNETS _____

Ten miles from the center of the nation's fifth largest city is a small valley with a murmuring creek, ringed with paths for people, pets and horses. In the spring, anglers line up on the banks of Wissahickon Creek to fish, but walking and jogging are the most common pursuits. Occasionally, a local geology class will be on an outing to learn about the tectonic events that shaped the metamorphic rocks of this valley and much of the rest of eastern Pennsylvania.

Wissahickon schist is the most common metamorphic rock in the valley, a part of the Fairmount Park system of the city of Philadelphia. Almandine garnets are abundant in the schist, but collectors more often find them weathered out. To get the feel and look of these little gems, take the Wise's Mill Road turn from Henry Avenue and park in the lot near the Valley Green Inn and the bridge that crosses the stream. From the lot, look across the stream and up the bank at a wood shelter. The path to the shelter starts on the other side of the bridge, to the left.

In the bluff opposite the shelter you can see Wissahickon schist in place. At the base of the bluff, in the sand on the path, and on top of the bluff are hundreds of garnets about one-half inch to microscopic in diameter. A little tumbling brings out the deep-red color of the stones. Try walking north or south of the shelter on the path, or search the gravel bars of the small streams that feed the Wissahickon Creek; garnets will be available wherever they have weathered out of the parent rock.

For a second location, return to Henry Avenue and turn right. In 1.3 miles, turn right onto Bell's Mill Road. Within a mile, there are two parking lots; the first one on the right is before the creek, and the second one, on the left, is just after the bridge that crosses the creek. Walk along the paths south of the road on either side of the creek. The garnets found in this area tend to be larger.

In the classic literature of this area (Bruce K. Goodwin's *Guidebook to the Geology of the Philadelphia Area*), there are sites to see staurolite, tourmaline, and kyanite as you walk up and down the Wissahickon Valley. Although many of those sites are no longer productive, it does not preclude looking. Feel the talc in one of the three large serpentine rocks at the edge of the path entering Andorra Natural Area at Bell's Mill Road. Talc and garnets are characteristic minerals formed during metamorphism. Staurolite forms exclusively in metamorphic rock.

While park rules posted at each of the roads do not specifically prohibit digging and using picks to break open the rocks, it is best to leave your shovels and hammers in the car and only take with you a collecting bag or film canister and a small awl.

Wissahickon Valley Garnets

Parking

Bell's Mill Rd.

1.0 Mi.

Parking

Garnets →

Trajl

N

W
I
S
S
A
H
I
C
K
O
N

1.3 Mi.

No cars!

CREEK

0.8 Mi.

Wise's Mill Rd.

Garnets

Parking

Valley Green
Inn

Valley Green Rd.

Map not to scale

PHOENIXVILLE DOLOMITE

Yellow to golden-brown, some say tan, curved dolomite crystals sprinkle the rock, but the prize is an inch-long clear quartz crystal nestled in the dolomite. Here is yet another classic example of mineral findings in the East. Simply put, keep your eye out for road cuts, tunnel excavations, and rock dumps. The dumps may not last very long; either the minerals cease to be interesting or the rock is carted away to be crushed for fill. During the years that it remains, a rock dump provides interesting collecting.

The Phoenixville lead-zinc district of Chester County is widely known in southeastern Pennsylvania. Most of the mines were on the same vein system and operated during the middle 1800s. The veins, consisting of sphalerite and galena in quartz at depth, cut into Precambrian granitic gneiss or Triassic red beds. Collectors on the lookout for mines or mine dumps with access today tramp golf courses, talk with cautious land owners, and stare despairingly at housing developments. It is refreshing to find a 15-feet high rock dump, which extends for more than 100 feet, to investigate.

True, we found no galena or sphalerite, but the quarter-inch to half-inch dolomite crystals suffice. It is the ferroan variety of dolomite, perhaps even ankerite. Iron replaces some of the magnesium in this carbonate of calcium and magnesium, so the color is not the usual dolomite pink. Formed in veins, the crystals hug the matrix and grow around massive quartz. Single quartz crystals occasionally rest in the dolomite. Pieces of goethite, another indicator of the source material, are found as well. Picking is easy; a hammer isn't necessary. From State Route 23 in Phoenixville, take State Route 29 north toward Collegeville. In various places along its route here, it may be called Bridge Street or Phoenixville-Collegeville Road. Within two miles, the road crosses under railroad tracks. Columbia Station is on the right before the tracks.

Rocks from a train tunnel excavation opposite the Columbia Station in Phoenixville.

Turn left immediately, and park your car on the right overlooking the Schuylkill River. Do not cross the bridge over the Schuylkill. Depending on conditions, you may be able to walk uphill to the tracks. The rock dumps are to your left or south. If this easy access is impossible, cross Route 29 very carefully and climb the pile from the park along the river. Watch for poison ivy and ticks.

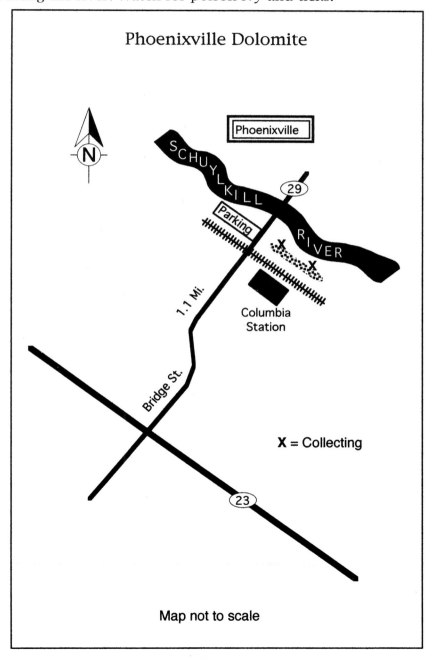

Phoenixville Dolomite

Phoenixville

SCHUYLKILL RIVER

29

Parking

Columbia Station

1.1 Mi.

Bridge St.

23

X = Collecting

Map not to scale

CHROME RUN MINERALS

The trickle of water known as Chrome Run southwest of Media in Riddlewood, Pennsylvania is a fine example of a collecting sight nearly overtaken by development. Unlike many other lost sites buried beneath parking lots, golf courses and housing developments, Chrome Run still yields a plentiful supply of minerals such as chromite, zircon and quartz crystals. Chrome Run flows between the Riddle Memorial Hospital and an apartment complex across from the Granite Run Mall on U.S. Highway 1, also known as the Baltimore Pike. The stream crosses the highway 0.4 mile from the intersection of U.S. Highway 1 with State Highway 452.

Finding the stream is easy. Parking is problematic. Chrome Run is surrounded by a rapidly developing area with entirely too many "no parking" signs. Once you stash your vehicle somewhere legal, you can make your way down to the stream by following the access road that leads to the apartments and walking down the grassy slope to Chrome Run. A small pool of water heads the stream here in front of a drainage pipe passing under the road.

Look for clusters of small quartz crystals as you walk down the slope and to the stream. The quartz is often stained deep red because of the chromite. Chromite is easy to spot in the stream, especially when the water is low. Look for black sand that gathers in pockets in the stream and on the bank. What at first looks like ordinary black dirt appears as multitudes of tiny octahedral chromite crystals under a hand lens or microscope. You can gather the crystals by panning or by scraping the black sand with a small trowel into a container and sorting later. The crystals are tiny to a few sixteenths-of-an-inch in diameter. Larger crystals are uncommon, though undoubtedly present in the stream gravel.

Chromite weathers from serpentine rocks in the area and collects in stream beds like Chrome Run. Before the turn-of-the-century, placer mines on this stream and a few others nearby worked the stream beds heavily. The miners removed as much as 500 tons of chromite before depleting the placers. Mining the chromite's host rock itself is impractical because it is not concentrated like the placers. The mines are gone, but the chromite continues to weather out and slowly make its way down stream.

In addition to chromite and small single or double terminated quartz crystals keep an eye out for a gemmy green variety of amphibole, serpentine, feldspar, and orange zircon grains. The zircon fluoresces yellow under short-wave ultraviolet light. Heavy vegetation makes searching down stream for any distance difficult, but not impossible in summer.

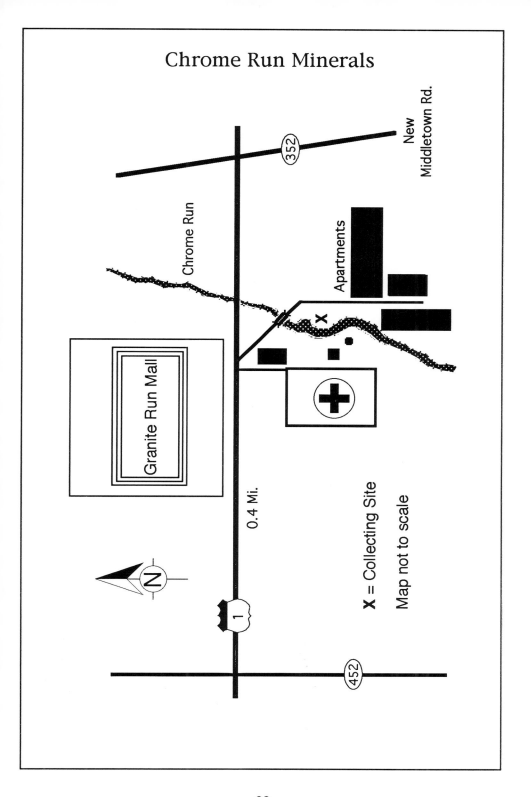

Chrome Run Minerals

X = Collecting Site

Map not to scale

Searching for chromite and quartz crystals along Chrome Run.

Collecting kyanite in the small stream that runs through Prospect Park.

PROSPECT PARK KYANITE _____

For many years local collectors visited a tiny tributary of Darby Creek in Prospect Park, Pennsylvania because of its rich supply of kyanite. The site is located beside the Morton Homestead on State Highway 420 in Prospect Park.

To reach the site from Interstate 476 (also called the Blue Route) use Exit 1 and travel east on MacDade Boulevard 2.8 miles to the intersection of State Highway 420. Turn right onto State Highway 420 and proceed 1.5 miles to the entrance to the Morton Homestead. There is a brown sign marking the park in the highway's center strip. Watch carefully for the sign—you only get one chance. If you approach from Interstate 95 onto State Highway 420, you will need to pass the site and turn around to enter the park.

Morton Homestead is a log cabin built by Swedish settlers of New Sweden in the 1600s. Interpretive writing at the park describes the history of the building and the homestead itself is open Wednesday to Saturday from April to October. An interesting sign marks the former bank of Darby Creek now a good distance from the water. Many people stop at the park to fish from the banks of Darby Creek, but are scarcely aware of the trickling tributary in a gully next to the parking area.

Silvery blue kyanite, present in many outcrops of the region's highly metamorphic terrain, is found throughout the stream gravel. The mouth of the stream is tidal and the gravel is covered with a thin, slippery layer of mud. To get your first view of kyanite, search in areas where running water has cleared the mud and look for the mineral's rectangular blades. The regular blade outlines are noticeable even when covered by mud.

A small garden claw is useful for digging into the gravel bars to get below the mud layer to expose more cystals. Most of the kyanite is partially stained a rusty iron red, but some of it retains a bright blue color. Don't dig with your hands and be careful when picking up a muddy piece of suspected kyanite. In years past, the streamside was used as a trash dump and there are many shards of glass in the stream that can resemble kyanite crystals when covered by mud.

Boulders mark a slight change in stream elevation as you search upstream and leave the tidal area and most of the mud behind. If you examine the boulders, you will notice that some contain fist-sized feldspar crystals. The pieces of kyanite tend to get larger as you move closer to State Highway 420. Kyanite of one to three inches in length and up to half-an-inch thick are frequently found and larger pieces of more than four inches were once common in the stream. The kyanite here is strongly associated with quartzite. Pieces of quartzite matrix with kyanite inclusions can make very attractive display pieces.

Prospect Park Kyanite

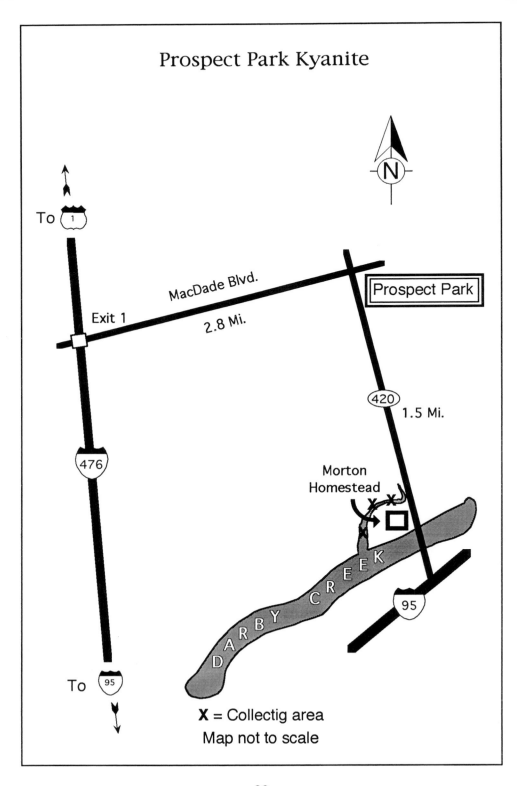

X = Collectig area
Map not to scale

A cluster of water-rinsed quartz crystals from the Crystal Point Diamond Mine.

Polished Cape May diamonds.

Devonian ammonite from the Williamsport area.

Dendrite formations on the Devonian rock near Williamsport.

Limonite bands from the Williamsport borrow pit.

Coatings of limonite give calcite crystals from the Eastern Industries Quarry a gem-like appearance.

Unusual sphalerite from Lime Crest Quarry is a translucent yellow-green.

Cut and polished picture sandstone found near Highland.

The vibrant fluorescent colors of Sterling Hill Mine ore gives it the nickname "Christmas Tree Ore." (Photo Credit: Ralph Thomas)

Ultraviolet light paints the fluorescent ore of the Franklin area. (Photo Credit: Ralph Thomas)

Carnelian quartz from Stirling Brook.

Shark teeth and invertebrate fossils from New Jersey.

A finely preserved brachiopod from Deer Lake.

Blue azurite and green malachite from a road cut near Rossville.

A cracked siderite concretion reveals platy barite crystals within.

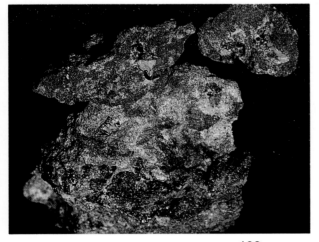

Pyrite crystals in matrix from the Morgantown spoils.

A lump of ruby is a welcome find at Lime Crest Quarry.

Blue-gray agate nodules from Mt. Holly Springs.

A sub-microscopic mixture of mica and serpentine makes "Eastonite."

Rich purple fluorite found in thin veins of New Paris quarry calcite.

A large vug of calcite from the Jersey Shore quarries.

Electric blue burns within a fine specimen of kyanite found at Prospect Park.

LIME CREST QUARRY

Lime Crest Quarry outside Sparta is one of the great mineral collecting sites of New Jersey. Thanks to the efforts of the Limestone Products Corporation and the Franklin-Ogdensburg Mineralogical Society, the site is open for collectors one Sunday in the spring and one in the fall (usually May and October). The quarry site, first commercially explored by Thomas Edison, primarily extracts a coarse-grained, Pre-Cambrian metamorphic limestone formation known as the Franklin Marble.

Quarrying at the vast Lime Crest pit reveals a blizzard of mineral specimens for collectors. Some common finds include calcite, graphite, chondrodite (brown to dark yellow specks), norbergite (pale yellow), fluorite (purple), pyrite, hornblende, spinel, sphalerite, ruby, blue apatite, dravite (a brown variety of tourmaline) and others. The quality, type and quantity of specimens change, as with all active quarries, when the quarry moves into new material. Each trip to Lime Crest will probably yield surprises.

There is no right or wrong way to collect at Lime Crest. Mineral specimens are everywhere and you can search in whatever way suits your style. Some collectors head right to the bottom and work up, others pick one of the terraced levels and work down, and still others pick a likely pile of boulders and begin a careful search. Collectors need to free most of the specimens from the host rock with a hammer and chisel. Newspapers to wrap the specimens will help prevent damage when placing them in a bucket or collecting bag. The quarry walls act as an oven on warm day. Take sufficient water with you in addition to food or snacks.

With all the minerals at Lime Crest to choose from the lapidary possibilities often get lost. Some of the quarry material with dark green or blue mineral inclusions makes an interesting cutting material. If you have a slab saw, pick up a piece and experiment. The soft stone is a relief for those accustomed to cutting agate and holds a good polish.

The only drawback to the wonderful collecting at Lime Crest is the long walk down to the quarry floor and even longer walk back up. The steep curving ramp is often an exhausting experience after a day's collecting. Many collectors bring wheelbarrows, carts, or wagons to help carry their finds. One of the best sights is a row of hammer-bearing rockhounds in hard hats pulling their little red wagons behind them at the start of the day. Don't chuckle too loud. You may be wishing for a wagon on the way back up.

The quarry open-house days are organized and supervised by the Franklin-Ogdensburg Mineralogical Society and open to members of other clubs. Each person must bring a valid membership card from a club that carries the group insurance policy offered by the Eastern Federation of Mineralogical Clubs and Lapidary Societies. This group insurance policy insures members of participating clubs belonging to the Eastern Federation. A single member of a participating club should represent the club and have a list of attending members. Each person must also bring a hard hat, safety shoes, safety glasses, and sign two liability releases before entering. Children below the age of twelve are not permitted in the quarry and older children must be supervised. Safety in the quarry is paramount so be alert as you are working and be considerate of those working near you. Stay away from all machinery and from the steep quarry walls. Loose rocks can drop without warning. Wearing a hard hat does not make you invulnerable and will not stop a falling boulder.

For more information and complete rules about the open house days at Lime Crest contact the Franklin-Ogdensburg Mineralogical Society, Box 146, Franklin, NJ 07416. Copy and distribute the information to your club members when possible rather than sending many individual letters. Do not contact the quarry or attempt to enter the quarry on days other than the open house.

The deep pit quarry at Lime Crest.

Lime Crest Quarry

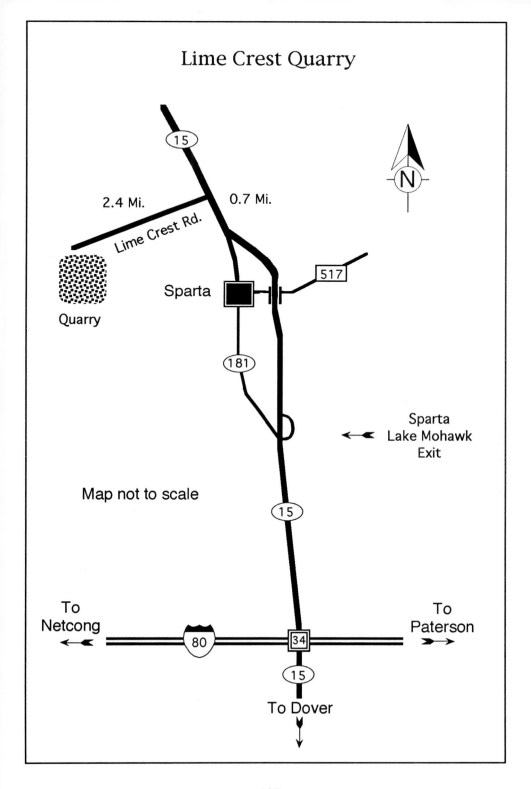

STERLING HILL MINE _____

The Sterling Hill Mine in Ogdensburg, New Jersey is the pinnacle of this region's amazing mineral collecting. The mine is just a short distance from either Franklin or Sparta off County Route 517. Turn north onto Passaic Avenue in Ogdensburg and travel 0.7 to the entrance for the Sterling Hill Mining Museum on the left.

Sterling Hill, named for Lord Stirling, an officer in Washington's army, overlooks the town of Ogdensburg on the western edge of the New Jersey Highlands. For some reason, both spellings of the name Stirling occur in place names throughout northern New Jersey. Large scale commercial mining of the Sterling Hill mine started around 1912 and concluded in 1986 with the New Jersey Zinc Company running the operation most of the time. Mine shafts penetrated 2,675 feet below ground and right beneath the town of Ogdensburg.

The Sterling Hill Mine, known in official records as the Sterling Mine, could easily have been lost to collectors if not for the efforts of the non-profit Sterling Hill Mining Museum that preserves the site. Museum workers rescued much of the original mining equipment and mineralized ore from the mine's lower levels. Once the mine's water pumps stopped, the lower shafts filled with water to a level about thirty feet below the surface.

Like a number of nearby mines and quarries, Sterling Hill Mine burrowed into the highly mineralized Franklin Marble formation. Mineralogists have identified 349 minerals from the Franklin-Ogdensburg area. The ore body at Sterling Hill is a mixture of franklinite, willemite, zincite and other minerals in calcite. The museum has a huge load of mineral-rich rock from the mine that collectors search for a fee. A pile of rock from other places including Lime Crest Quarry is also at the collecting site.

Octahedral franklinite crystals, resembling chocolate chips, abound in the calcite. Other minerals that collectors are likely to encounter include willemite (brown), zincite (dark red), rhodonite (rose), gahnit (dark green), apatite (blue-green) and galena (silver). The vast assemblage of minerals available almost always guarantees a few surprises. At least 70 minerals of the Franklin-Ogdensburg area fluoresce (see Buckwheat Dump). The area has perhaps the most brilliant fluorescent minerals found anywhere. Calcite fluoresces bright red-orange, willemite fluoresces bright green and hydrozincite fluoresces blue— for just a small sample of the possibilities. A portable short-wave light will help to find the best fluorescent specimens. The museum provides a dark room at the collecting site for this purpose. Rock blasted from the mine's new Edison Tunnel is open to collecting periodically for

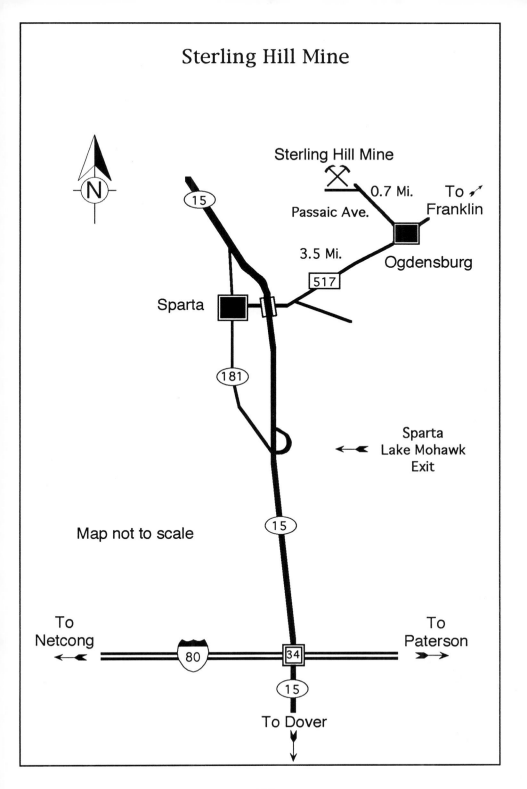

members of the Sterling Hill Mining Museum Foundation.

Collecting days at the museum are on the last Sunday of the month (the museum is not open all winter). A reasonable fee allows collectors to take ten pounds of rock. Additional rock costs another dollar per pound. It doesn't take long to get ten pounds of minerals because the ore is extremely heavy!

Whether you plan to collect or not, do not miss the opportunity to go on the museum mine tour. The mining museum building (separate from the gift shop) is open by tour only and gives visitors a chance to view hundreds of fine specimens and get an overview of the mining operation. The tour also plunges below ground into the upper levels of the mine. At one point in the tour, the tour guide illuminates ore-laced walls of the shaft with ultraviolet light and produces a rainbow of magnificent color.

Special collecting days are sometimes possible for larger groups with advance arrangements. Contact the mine at (973) 209-7212 or write to the Sterling Hill Mine and Museum, 30 Plant Street, Ogdensburg, NJ 07439.

More than 300 minerals are found at Sterling Hill Mine.

BUCKWHEAT DUMP

The zinc mines near Franklin, New Jersey have true world-class status because of their incredible variety of minerals, fine crystallization, and colorful fluorescence. Not all of the old mine dumps are open regularly, but thanks to the Franklin Mineral Museum, collectors can pay a small fee and visit the Buckwheat Dump any time that the museum is open.

To reach the Franklin Mineral Museum from State Route 23, turn west onto County Route 631 (Franklin Avenue) and travel to Buckwheat Road. Turn north onto Buckwheat and then left in 0.1 mile onto Evans road The museum parking lot is straight ahead. Access to the mine dump is through the museum and down a long set of railroad tie stairs.

The ore on the mine dump is part of the Franklin Marble, a Precambrian Formation. Miners of the New Jersey Zinc Company worked the mine shafts to a depth of more than 1200 feet. Mining ceased in 1954 as the supply of ore became exhausted. Recreational collectors have exhausted themselves working on the mine dumps ever since. About one-hundred and fifty mineral species are present at the mine and new minerals are still being described.

Just a brief inspection of the mine dumps reveals calcite embedded with franklinite, willemite and other minerals. Collectors have worked these dumps for many years and it is a testament to the richness of the ore that good material is easily found. If you plan to search for prize specimens, be prepared for extra effort. The best way to begin is to find a pit that somebody else has already started and begin clearing material from the bottom.

For many, the most exciting aspect of Franklin minerals is their high degree of fluorescence and phosphorescence. Some minerals react to ultraviolet light by emitting colors. This happens because the ultraviolet light affects the mineral on the atomic level. Energy from the light disrupts the moving structure of electrons in the mineral's atoms. As the electrons try to reorient themselves, they release energy that we can see as visible light. The mineral emits its own light and does not merely reflect it. Calcite and willemite, two of the most common fluorescent minerals in the mine spoils, fluoresce a bright red and green respectively. Some of the minerals continue emitting light for a few seconds to minutes after the ultraviolet light is switched off. The effect, called phosphorescence, occurs when the electrons take a longer time to stabilize in their orbits.

Collecting fluorescent minerals is easier with a portable ultraviolet light. Battery operated ultraviolet lights are available in many rock shops and through mail-order catalogs. There are two types of

Buckwheat Dump

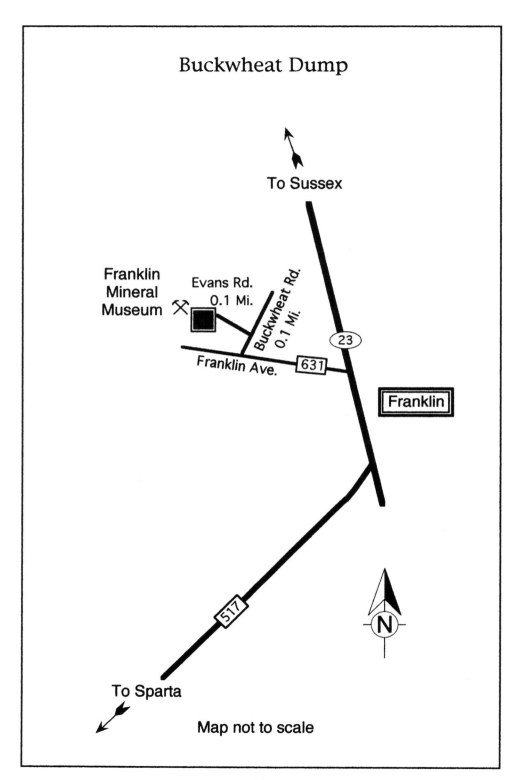

To Sussex

Franklin Mineral Museum

Evans Rd. 0.1 Mi.

Buckwheat Rd. 0.1 Mi.

Franklin Ave.

631

23

Franklin

517

To Sparta

N

Map not to scale

ultraviolet lights—long-wave and short-wave, and different minerals will react with each. Most fluorescent minerals react with short-wave ultraviolet light. Unless bringing a combination unit with both types of light, bring a short-wave light. Ultraviolet lighting works best in total darkness. The museum provides a dark room adjacent to the mine dump to help collectors examine collected specimens under ultraviolet light. Some people bring a dark blanket to examine rocks out on the dumps without walking to the dark room. Although it seems odd, it will make the work easier. Short-wave ultraviolet light is similar to the type of light that causes sunburn. Do not look directly into the light.

The museum has a magnificent mineral collection on display and one of the finest fluorescent mineral exhibits found anywhere. It is a good idea to visit the museum before collecting to get a "feel" for the minerals out on the mine dumps. The museum charges $5.00 for adults and $2.50 for children to collect on the mine dumps. The fee entitles adults to collect 25 pounds of rock for the price and children may take ten pounds. The museum also sells a combination ticket for the museum and mineral collecting. The museum is open spring through fall and groups should phone in advance. To find out about specific times and dates call the museum at (973)827-3481 or write Franklin Mineral Museum, P. O. Box 54, Franklin, NJ 07416.

The Buckwheat Dump in Franklin.

LAKE VALHALLA YELLOW SERPENTINE

A swampy trail and uphill walk lead to an interesting locality for green, black, and gemmy yellow serpentine. The quarry dumps are overgrown now, but the quarry site is still visible. The lower end of the quarry encompasses a pegmatite that yields well-formed hornblende crystals. Minerals reported at the quarry include malachite, pyrite, bornite, diaspore, aragonite, quartz, asbestos, and talc in addition to the hornblende. Serpentine, mica, and feldspar are still available with a hammer, sledgehammer, chisel, and eye protection.

The quarry is now part of the Morris County, New Jersey park system and the trails to it are maintained, though swampy enough to require boots in rainy weather. From Interstate 287 take Exit 47 to Montville. Drive 0.2 mile on U.S. Highway 202, then take Valhalla Road north. In another 0.2 mile go under the railroad

Follow Valhalla Road around to the left. Four-tenths of a mile past the railroad overpass, you will go through stone pillars marking a gateway for an older housing development. You are now on Vista Road. Turn right on Lake Shore Drive. The distance along the shoreline of Lake Valhalla is 0.8 mile. At Hemlock Road, bear right and immediately turn left for a 100-yard drive into a one car parking area located between two houses. This is the trail head.

A ten minute walk takes you to a trail intersection. Stay on the green marker trail. The bottom part of the quarry will soon be visible on your right. Another ten-minute walk takes you to the red marker trail. To the right is a small trail leading to the top part of the quarry. The total distance on the trail is about 0.5 mile.

Fall, winter, and early spring are good times to visit because of the

plant growth. In all those seasons, you still have to contend with the leaf cover that is significant. According to previous collectors, the serpentine is good for cutting, carving and making cabochons. Several small pieces of black and yellow serpentine recently collected are gemmy enough to take a fine polish.

A chunk of yellow serpentine.

Lake Valhalla Yellow Serpentine

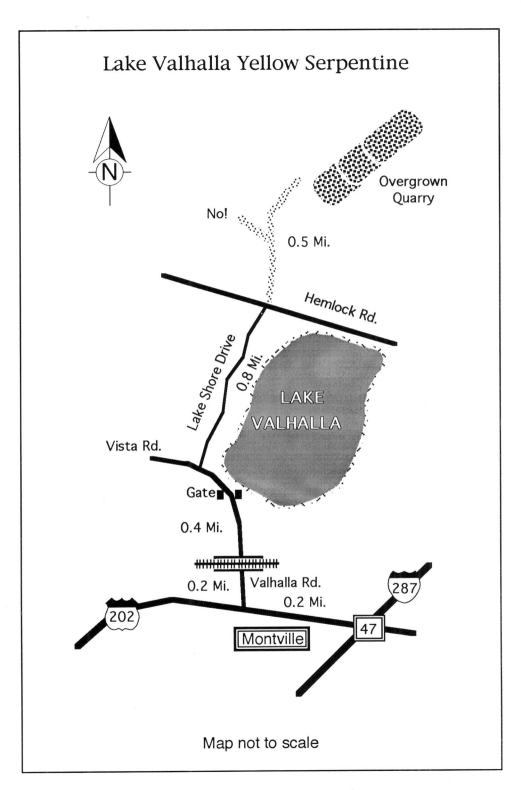

Map not to scale

BASALT QUARRY MINERALS _____

The lure of productive trap rock quarries in New Jersey is irresistible, even if some of those venerable locations are covered with water, parking lots, or buildings. Basalt was the "trap rock" mined for a hundred years in these quarries and used for construction and roads. The variety and beauty of zeolites and associated minerals found in basalt cavities is the attraction for mineral collectors.

At Montclair State University, the edges of student parking lot #25 still yield minerals associated with a former basalt quarry. Calcite, quartz, malachite, chrysocolla, glauberite casts, hematite, stilbite and heulandite are collecting possibilities.

Visiting is best done on a weekend or when school is not in session. It is important to contact the school's campus police office at (973)655-5222, from 7:00 a.m. to 3:00 p.m. weekdays. Obtain a "hold harmless form" from the office that allows you to be there but not hold the University responsible for your safety.

Thick basalt sheets of the Watchung Mountain deposits in New Jersey are the source of the finest zeolites in this country. Sequences of sandstones, shales, and basalt were deposited during the Triassic period. As water solutions entered the 200-million-year-old lava flows, sulfates, sulfides, oxides, carbonates, and silicates precipitated out in crystal forms.

Today, what was once known as the Upper Montclair Basalt Quarry is two parking lots and the site of the Floyd Hall Arena. A short walk around the perimeter of both parking lots to look at the rubble and rock cuts on the edge of the asphalt gives one a glimpse of the minerals found in the quarry's heyday.

The best collecting is done at the wall of the former quarry's east side, in the parking area of the Arena. Vugs the size of golf balls in the basalt contain fine micromount specimens of calcite crystals and zeolites such as heulandite and stilbite. Deep purple amethyst crystals that are present measure about a half-inch.

There is no need to cross the fence and climb down the steep dangerous walls from lot #25. Use the road! Easy walking and careful observation yields samples of the copper minerals malachite and chrysocolla, red hematite, and forms of quartz. Quartz from one of the six deposition periods is found as smoky quartz, amethyst, agate, and opal. A good find for the mineral enthusiast is a quartz pseudomorph of glauberite. The rhombic cavities tell the story of beautiful crystals dissolving after being encrusted with quartz.

Montclair State University is located south of the intersection of U.S. Highway 46 and Valley Road in West Paterson. Turn right on Normal Avenue, 1.1 mile south of U.S. 46. The University is on the

Basalt Quarry Minerals

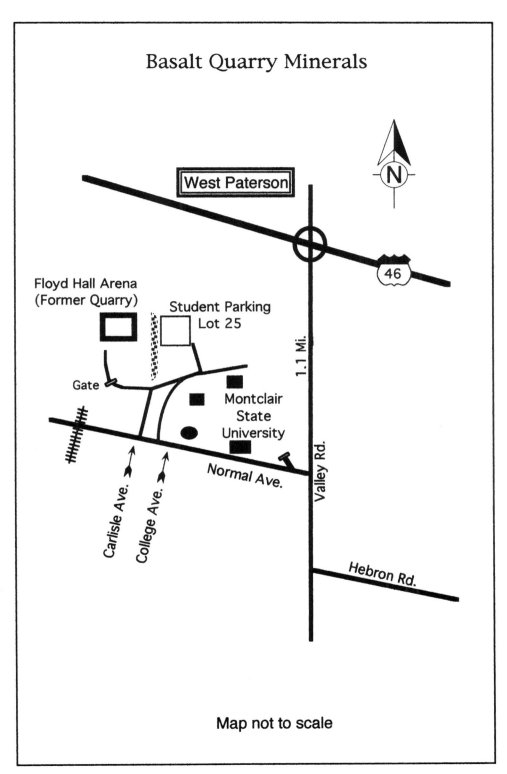

right. Follow College Avenue (one-way) to the north and to parking lot #25, a left turn. Road access to the Floyd Hall Arena parking lot is from the rear of lot #25 at the time of publication. If you find yourself without a car, visit this site by taking a New Jersey Transit train. The Montclair Heights Station is on Normal Avenue, west of the College Avenue or Carlisle Avenue routes to the Arena and parking lots.

Part of the quarry floor is a parking lot.

Many small copper mines surfaced in New Jersey's Watchung Mountains with the discoveries of small copper sulfide veins. One of the country's earliest copper mines, started in 1712, was also a large one. The Schuyler Copper Mine, of what is now North Arlington, New Jersey, tunneled into part of a ridge paralleling State Highway 17.

Some authors say it is the first mine of any real value discovered after nearly a century of prospecting by the colonists. According to a New Jersey State Geological Bulletin, the Schuyler family operated the mine, to some extent profitably, until about 1753, after which other operators leased it. It passed out of the family's hands in the early 1800s and occasionally operated as a mine until 1901.

The mine opening, filled in some years ago, is no longer visible and houses cover the old tunnels. The remainder of the mine dumps on the east side of the ridge are now the back of an industrial park. Industries line the base of the ridge, west of a landfill and Hackensack Meadows.

The copper ore at the Schuyler Mine is associated with sandstone layers that overlie a Triassic diabase known as the Arlington diabase sill. The Triassic sediments include brownish gray sandstones, composed of quartz and feldspars, with interbedded red shales. The Arlington sill created fractures resulting in copper mineral deposition. Probably both the Arlington diabase and the Schuyler copper minerals had their origin in the Palisade sill that lies under this locality.

From State Highway 17 in North Arlington, take Belleville Turnpike east for 0.5 mile to Schuyler Avenue. To get your bearings in this landscape, turn left onto Schuyler Avenue and take either Morton or Avon Roads to the right. At the dead ends, the industrial park, Hackensack Meadows and the landfill are all visible to the east. The old mine dumps were below here.

Go back to Belleville Turnpike, turn left, and continue 0.1 mile to Porete Avenue, the access road to the industrial park. Bear left on Porete Avenue. You can travel a total of 0.5 mile on the industrial park roadway, passing by many businesses. The "for sale" sign at the northern end of the road suggests there may be more industries here in the future. It is possible to find access to the side and base of the ridge without entering locked gates or crossing any "no trespassing" signs.

Chrysocolla is the most common mineral, found as a green coating on sandstone. Other copper minerals present are malachite and chalcocite and, rarely, azurite. Botryoidal crusts of conichalcite are still found. Reports of covellite and brochantite are in the literature. Besides copper minerals, calcite, selenite, epidote, and pyrolusite dendrites are also possible from the mine dumps.

Schuyler Copper Mine Dumps

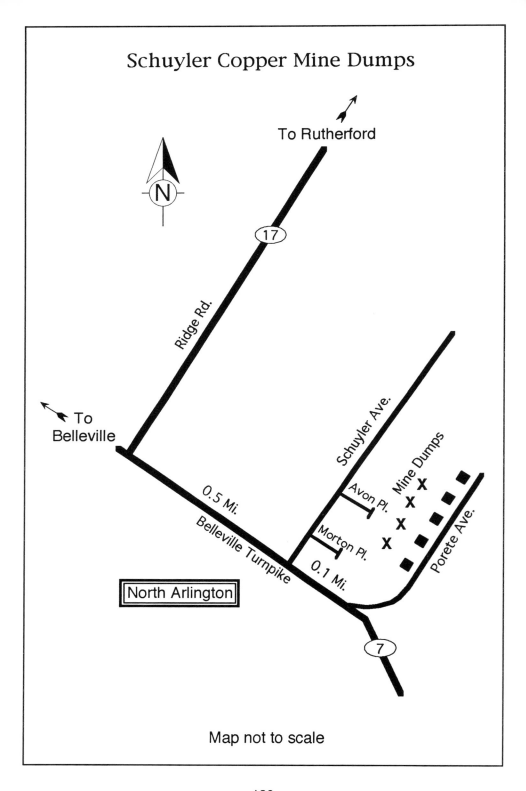

To Rutherford

N

17

Ridge Rd.

To Belleville

0.5 Mi.

Belleville Turnpike

North Arlington

Schuyler Ave.

Mine Dumps

Avon Pl.

Morton Pl.

0.1 Mi.

Porete Ave.

7

Map not to scale

Copper ore specimens from the Schuyler Copper Mine dumps.

Hunting for carnelian in Stirling Brook.

STIRLING BROOK CARNELIAN _____

Collectors have visited Stirling Brook in Somerset County, New Jersey for decades to search for the yellow-red carnelian found there. The little stream, sometimes referred to as "Carnelian Brook" by collectors, is still a productive location for carnelian and a variety of other quartz and chalcedony.

Stirling Brook near Watchung is not the easiest place to find because of a very confusing traffic circle in Watchung. Take County Route 531 (Watchung Avenue) from North Plainfield or U.S. Highway 22 and travel to the traffic circle in Watchung. Exit the circle on the third road labeled County Route 653 or Stirling Road beside Lake Watchung. There is an Old Stirling Road west of the circle so don't be confused if you travel from that direction.

The bridge across Stirling Brook is 1.4 miles from the circle. Avoid the tavern property next to the brook and park instead behind a shopping center on Community Place, the road immediately after the bridge. You can cross to the brook through a power line cut behind the shopping center. The undergrowth and mosquitoes are dense in the woods surrounding Stirling Brook in summer time. Avoid the private property that borders the stream.

The stream bed of Stirling Brook has brown to red carnelian, white chalcedony, agate, small quartz crystals, smoky quartz and amethyst. In order to find the minerals, you need to use a box screen to sift sediments from the stream bottom (see appendix). Holes from other collectors are evident on the stream bank. It is a wet and dirty job so come prepared with a screen, shovel, specimen container or bucket, change of clothes and boots in cool weather. A walk up or down stream may reveal gravel bars that make collecting easier and may possibly yield some fresh material.

The minerals found in the creek weather out of the mineralized Watchung basalt that covers much of northern New Jersey. Most of the carnelian and other quartz are thumb-nail size or smaller. Larger pieces of carnelian are few, but reveal a warm red or golden color and make exceptional tumbled stones and cabochons. The reddish color of the carnelian is probably the result of hematite present in the chalcedony.

Watchung agates tend to be small, but highly colorful and banded. Like the carnelian, larger New Jersey agates make beautiful polished stones. The small smoky quartz and amethyst crystals range from pale to very dark, especially in the case of the smoky quartz. Complete crystals are scarce.

Stirling Brook Carnelian

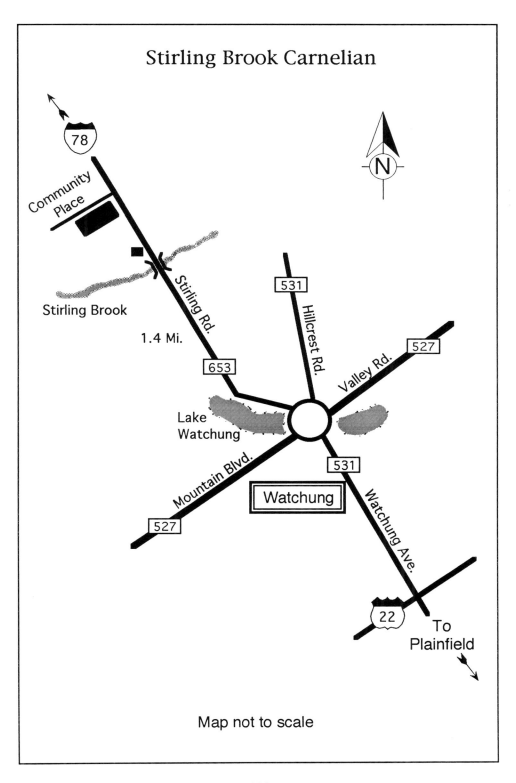

Map not to scale

Outcrops of Late Cretaceous sedimentary formations in New Jersey host a number of minerals including marcasite, pyrite and the stone formation known as an "Indian paint pot." The shoreline of Raritan Bay, at Cliffwood Beach, exposes dark silty clays of the Magothy Formation where marcasite nodules were once possible. Unfortunately, weathering, erosion and shoreline jetties have made marcasite a scarce find, but the site may still be worth a visit if you are in the area.

The Cliffwood Beach collecting site is 1.0 mile north of State Highway 35 in Cliffwood. Turn north onto Cliffwood Avenue from State Highway 35. The road changes from Cliffwood Avenue in 0.5 mile to S. Concourse, presumably short for Shore Concourse, and continues another 0.5 mile to the water. Turn right and park beside a jetty at the water's edge across from Keyport Harbor. A gate prevents you from driving far in this direction. Another parking area is a short distance up Beach Drive in the opposite direction. The distant shoreline visible across Raritan Bay is Staten Island, New York.

The Magothy Formation extends south from this point through New Jersey and as far as the shores of the Chesapeake Bay. Geologists first identified the outcrops in the Raritan Bay area as early as 1904. Commercial clay pits that worked portions of the Magothy, known as the Amboy Clay, were once excellent collecting areas for large pyrite nodules. Development has almost entirely covered these productive clay pits. As always, collectors should watch for recent diggings in the area that may expose the dark mineralized clay of the Magothy Formation.

Collecting at Cliffwood Beach is easy, but not nearly as productive as in years gone by. Engineers building the sea wall excavated and used Magothy material for their project. As a result, the wall was once sprinkled with heavy marcasite nodules. Most of this material has washed away, but there is still a chance that some of the material may wash up. Marcasite and pyrite nodules may be round, long and thin, or just odd-shaped blobs that can weigh more than three pounds! You may need to train your eyes to spot the nodules, especially if the golden color is not showing through the silt.

At one time, the bluff area behind the jetty was a collecting site for siderite concretions with marine fossils. Nothing much is there now because of housing and jetty construction, but occasional fossils do wash up on the beach and any of the areas along the jetty exposed at low tide. Chunks of sandstone on the beach, probably from the upper part of the formation, contain fragmentary marine fossils. The sandstone on the beach has small hollow pockets that, when broken,

Cliffwood Beach

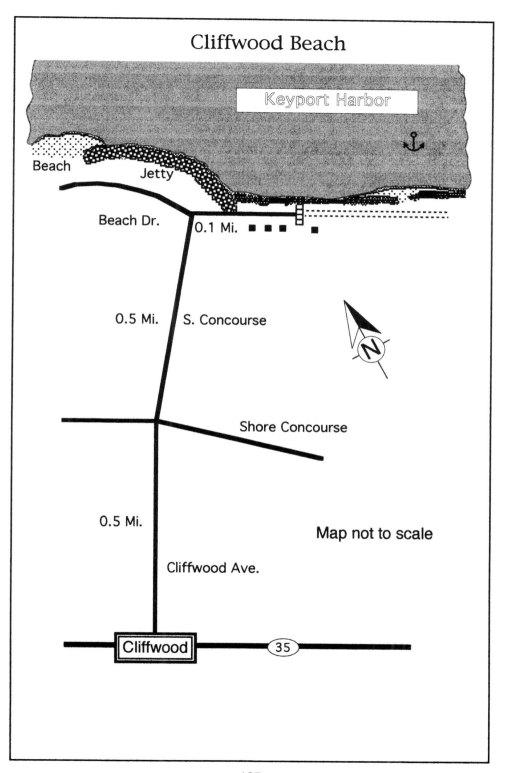

resemble a bowl or tube sometimes called an "Indian paint pot." Collectors should also be aware of the many important amber finds in the region. A fossil ant found preserved in sequoia amber near Cliffwood Beach in 1966 provided important information concerning the evolution of ants. Area amber finds continue to generate considerable scientific interest.

Other insects of note include biting green flies that spring and early summer bring to Raritan Bay. Be prepared with long pants and repellent at that time of year.

Collecting along the shoreline at Cliffwood Beach.

PORICY PARK FOSSIL BEDS _____

The most friendly place for collecting fossils in New Jersey is also a well-known place. From the directions and hand outs provided by the Poricy Park Nature Center, to the visible and well-maintained parking area, it is easy to collect at Poricy Brook.

Fossils in the stream are from the exposed Navesink Formation of the Cretaceous period. The fossils are remains of marine animals that lived approximately 72 million years ago. A shallow ocean covered what is now the Atlantic coastal plain during that time. The most common fossils are invertebrates such as pelecypods, gastropods, cephalopods, and brachiopods. Shark teeth are the usual vertebrate finds, though they are rare. Oyster species sure to be found are *Exogyra costata*, *Pycnodonte (Gryphaea) convexa*, and *Agerostrea mesenterica*. *Turitella* snails are rare and found as internal casts. Internal guards of ancient squid-like animals *Belemnitella americana* look like amber-colored pens, stained with iron. The brachiopod frequently found is *Choristothyris plicata*, which looks like a small clam shell.

The best way to find fossils is by digging in the stream bed and sifting the sand and gravel in a screen box (see appendix). The nature center asks people collecting at Poricy Park not to dig into the stream banks. The best time of year to collect is in early spring. Nature center staff also asks collectors to take home only a handful of specimens, so that other collectors may discover these ancient creatures. Children enjoy collecting in Poricy Brook and guided fossil trips are popular events at the nature center. Groups on their own must notify the nature center of their trips to avoid overcrowding.

Parking for the Fossil Beds is on Middletown Lincroft Road in Middletown, New Jersey. From State Highway 35, between Keyport and Red Bank, take Oak Hill Road west past the nature center and two

railroad tracks to Middletown Lincroft Road. Turn left and travel 0.3 mile to the parking area. The stream is south of the parking area.

You will need a shovel, screen box, shoes that can get wet, and a small bag for specimens.

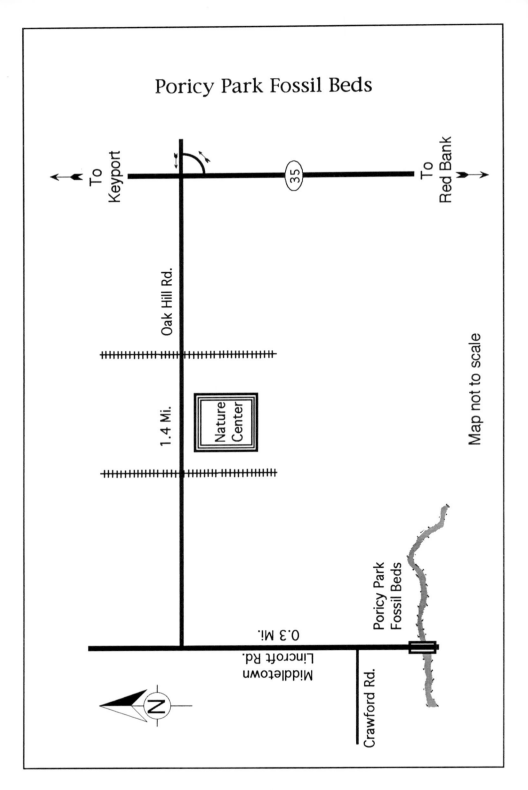

Poricy Park Fossil Beds

site 44 BIG BROOK FOSSIL SHARK TEETH

Little distinguishes the slowly rolling waters of Big Brook from the many other meandering streams of New Jersey. From a bridge overlooking the brook, the stream bed looks perfectly ordinary except for an abundance of fallen trees. The stream's continued erosion deep into the Monmouth County countryside causes trees on the bank to topple into the stream. The same erosion makes Big Brook a productive source of Cretaceous shark teeth and has for decades. As Big Brook carves its way through the layers of New Jersey sediment, it bites into sections of the Marshalltown, Wenonah and Mount Laurel-Navesink Formations.

Travel north from Freehold, New Jersey on State Highway 79. Look for Vandenberg Road in Marlboro soon after the State Highway 18 overpass and turn right. In 3.3 miles, turn left onto Hillsdale Road. The parking area is 0.6 mile on the east side of the road. Very limited parking is also available on the roadside northeast of the Boundary Road bridge.

Park in the open area on the east side of Hillsdale Road at a township park trail. From there collectors can follow the trail downstream or wade in the water upstream to collecting sites. The entire stream bed has fossils, so no matter where you begin you will almost always find some.

For most, the big attraction of Big Brook is the chance of finding fossil shark teeth. It is difficult at best to walk around and simply pick up shark teeth and other vertebrate fossils. Although plentiful, fossil hunters can walk in the creek all day and never see one.

To find vertebrate fossils and smaller invertebrate fossils you will need to use a box screen and shovel (see appendix). Sift shoveled sediments from the stream bottom with the box screen and wash it in the water. The sediment falls away leaving the larger stones and fossils behind. As you travel the stream, you will see piles of discarded stones where others have collected.

Fossil teeth are more common the farther you travel up stream. Look for gravel bars and a solid gravel stream bottom before you start shoveling. Avoid areas of heavy silt. After you have washed the gravel thoroughly, toss out the larger debris and dip it into the water one final time. Search the screen for fossils. It may take a while to train your eye to recognize the darker toothy shapes hidden in the gravel.

Collectors occasionally find large specimens, but most of the teeth are one inch long or less. The most common teeth found in the creek are the broad-bladed *Squalicorax* and longer, pointy sand shark teeth. Other types of vertebrates found at Big Brook include fish, turtle, stingray, crocodile, mosasaur, plesiosaur and rare dinosaur fossils.

Invertebrate fossils are more frequent as you travel downstream from the parking area on Hillsdale. Large specimens of the fossil shell *Exogyra* up to five inches long are common in stream gravel and banks. The internal shells of fossil squid called *Belemnitella americana* are also numerous. Belemnites resemble translucent spear points. Large invertebrate fossils are easy to find by walking in the shallow water. Screening will also turn up smaller invertebrate fossils like sea urchin spines, crustaceans and small shells.

Big Brook winds its way through areas of well-marked private land. New Jersey law allows passage through the stream bed even if the surrounding land is privately owned. The law does not allow collectors to trespass outside the stream. If you're not sure about the land's ownership, stay in the stream.

Water levels fluctuate depending on the season and the amount of rainfall. The best time to visit is after the spring runoff and before cold weather from June to October. Bring insect repellent in the warmer months and wear shoes in the creek because of broken glass.

Collectors screen gravel for shark teeth.

Big Brook Fossil Shark Teeth

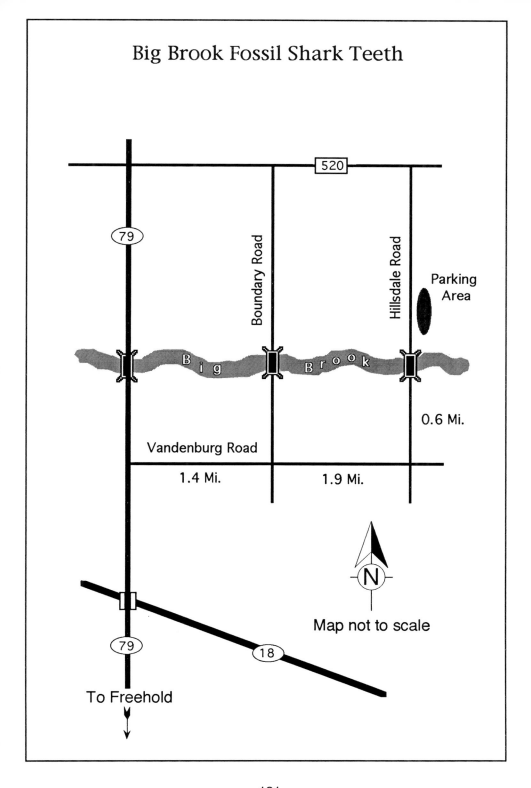

PINE BARRENS BOG IRON

Let's face it. Bog iron is not very appealing to the eye. It looks exactly like the lump of iron-filled sandstone that it is. There are no visible crystals in it and it is not shiny or colorful. Two hundred years ago it was so much in demand that whole towns arose in the New Jersey Pine Barrens to support the iron industry. Most of those towns are gone or lost now. New trees replace those burned as charcoal to fuel the furnaces. Everything changed when a purer grade of iron, located near anthracite fields, made neighboring Pennsylvania famous and prosperous.

Exploring the Pine Barrens today you will not find many remnants of the iron industry, but large pieces of bog iron still line cellars of old houses. Bog iron rocks border driveways of modern houses. If you mention a desire to find a piece of bog iron, someone will invite you over to take all you want from their fields. So why would you go searching for some on your own?

Minerals in the Pine Barrens are few unless you count the micro-minerals in sand. Bog iron is unique, as is this wilderness located in the most densely populated state of the United States. From Chatsworth, the heart of the Pines, take County Route 563 south to Burlington County Route 679, a distance of almost 10 miles. Turn left and travel 1.8 miles to the sand road marked by a sign for Bodine Field. Between the highway right-of-way and the power company's right-of-way are chunks of bog iron. They are in the sand of the unpaved road and on the banks of the road. Only surface collecting of bog iron is allowed.

It is gritty looking and reddish brown in color, nothing more than sandstone containing a soluble form of iron. Chemically, bog iron is a variety of limonite, formed in the slow-moving waters of the acidic cedar bogs of the Pine Barrens. Some say that it takes only 25 years for an ore bed to form.

To see some of that cedar water for yourself, take the sand road to the left, to the canoe takeout spot called Beaver Branch. To the right is Bodine Field, a group campsite in Wharton State Forest. Beaver Branch and Bodine Field are on the banks of the Wading River. An alternate method of finding bog iron is to walk in the Wading River and pick up pieces from the gravel you step on. Passenger cars may have difficulty navigating the sandy roads of the Pine Barrens. Thick white sand, called sugar sand, can mire a vehicle in seconds.

Pine Barrens Bog Iron

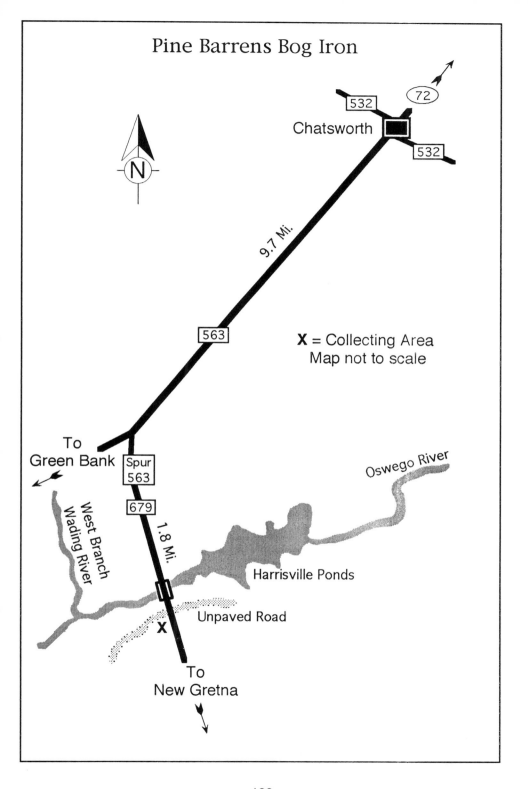

X = Collecting Area
Map not to scale

The squat shape of the cooling tower belonging to the Salem Hope Creek Power Station 10 miles south of Salem, New Jersey is mitigated only by the beauty of the surrounding marshlands. A small and little-known beach beside the power plant is a collecting area for wave tumbled jasper and colorful quartzite. The area around the power plant is known locally as "Artificial Island" because of the extensive fill used to construct the site on the shores of Delaware Bay. A semi-circle of sunken barges surround the beach as a water break to slow erosion.

To reach the site, travel 4.5 miles south on County Route 658 from Salem, New Jersey and turn right at Alloway Creek Neck Road. The road here expands into a three-lane highway leading to the power plant. Alloway Creek Neck Road divides in 5.3 miles. Stay right and then, turn left at the traffic light. Do not continue down the road leading right. Access to the small beach is through a path 0.4 mile farther on the left.

Some of the stones on the red sand beach probably tumbled south from as far away as New York. Others are easily recognizable as jasper from Pennsylvania and many more are probably part of the vast load of glacial outwash deposited after the last Ice Age sheet receded. The most abundant stone is quartzite. Quartzite is an often overlooked or maligned stone. The quartzite here, however, is a great stone for tumbling. The color ranges from gray to black, white and red. Much of the quartzite is banded.

Quartz pebbles about one inch and smaller are the second most common stone. They range from opaque and milky to perfectly clear when polished. Jasper is never as plentiful as the other stones, but a little searching will almost always turn some up. The jasper is light to dark red, yellow or brown. Some of the jasper has fine dendritic lines running through it and is especially interesting when polished.

The best collecting is at low tide when larger areas of stone are exposed. It is tricky to gauge when the tide will be in or out here unless you time it the day before. Tidal creeks crossed on the trip down from Salem may be at high tide, while the beach on the bay is at low tide and vice versa. The low tide advantage is also very short lived before the tide rushes back in and covers the stones again. The end result is usually a tidal hit or miss game. Fortunately, stones are visible above the high tide mark too. If you are lucky enough to arrive when the tide is low and are tempted to walk onto any of the closer sunken barges—beware. A thin layer of slick mud covers the wooden areas and there are many sharp metal projections inside.

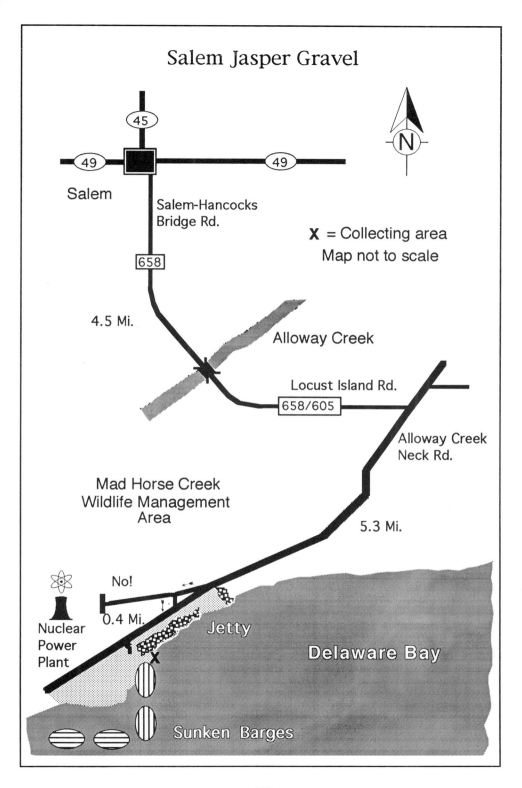

Salem Jasper Gravel

45

49   49

Salem

Salem-Hancocks
Bridge Rd.

658

X = Collecting area
Map not to scale

4.5 Mi.

Alloway Creek

Locust Island Rd.

658/605

Alloway Creek
Neck Rd.

Mad Horse Creek
Wildlife Management
Area

5.3 Mi.

No!

Nuclear
Power
Plant

0.4 Mi.

Jetty

Delaware Bay

X

Sunken Barges

Much of the surrounding area falls within the boundary of the nearly 6,000 acres of state owned land called Mad Horse Creek Wildlife Management Area. As a result, you may see many people fishing, hunting or bird watching in parts of the management area during the proper seasons. Insect repellent is a must if you visit the location from spring to fall. If there is a breeze from the bay, you will probably not spot a single biting insect. If the breeze is absent, they will spot you. Green flies populate the marshes from late spring to early summer and can turn a visit into a nightmare without long pants, sleeves and repellent.

Collecting jasper and quartzite near the row of sunken barges.

CAPE MAY DIAMONDS

The most common mineral found on Cape May, New Jersey's beaches has earned the label "diamond" because it is uncommonly clear and beautiful. Quartz pebbles found on the beaches of Cape May County have true gem quality and are eagerly sought by rockhounds. The best place to find Cape May diamonds is on Sunset Beach, west of Cape May, at the end of Sunset Boulevard.

The beach gravels of Sunset Beach are tumbled Delaware River Valley sediments that probably had their origins in northern New Jersey, Pennsylvania and New York. Clear quartz crystals, broken into pieces, became part of the alluvial material that traveled south in the glacial erosion of the Pleistocene Ice Age. Yellow Pleistocene gravel covers large areas of South Jersey, but the wind and waves of Delaware Bay are responsible for transforming the limonite-stained pieces of rounded quartz into the clear beach pebbles so many seek.

Native Americans were the first people fascinated with the stones. European interest began when King Nummy, a chief of the Lenni Lenape Indians, made a gift of one to Christopher Leaming. It is said that when Mr. Leaming's stone was cut, the name Cape May diamond was born. For more than a hundred years, visitors to the area have been engaged in the pursuit of diamonds.

Sunset Beach couldn't be more convenient for the collector. There is a free parking lot, a snack bar and restrooms inside a gift shop. The displays in the shop can be your starting point, for here you can see the stones in their naturally semipolished state, or polished and cut into faceted gemstones. A short walk onto the beach toward the exposed remains of the sunken ship SS *Atlantis* takes you to the first collecting site. The ship rests in the water off the beach beyond a small jetty. Look in the damp gravel around the jetty for pebbles that shine like glass or diamond.

Cape May diamonds are usually pebble to marble sized. Polished agate and jasper, rounded shark's teeth, horn coral, amethyst and Indian arrowheads are also found on area beaches. Collecting can be done year-round.

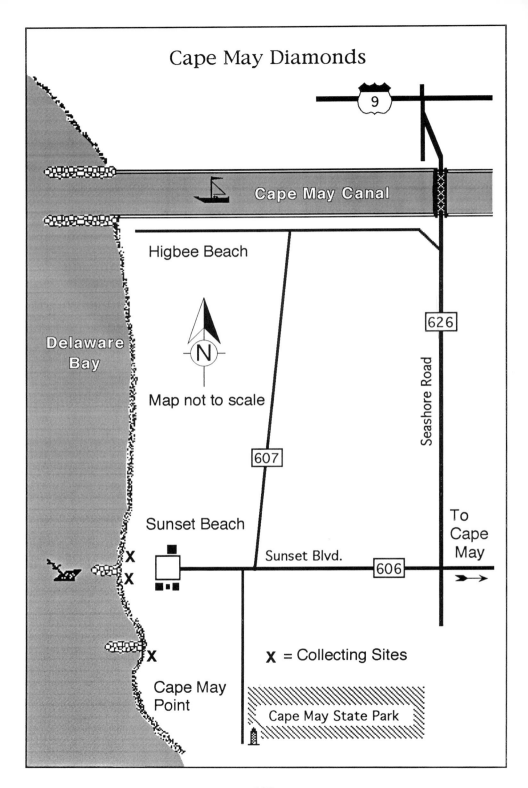

Cape May Diamonds

BUILDING A SCREEN BOX _____

A screen box used to sift sediments is essential at collecting sites such as Sterling Brook, Poricy Park, Big Brook and others. Building a screen box is a fairly simple procedure with only a few tools and materials needed. The size of the screen box can vary according to the individual's taste, but a broad surface area will simplify collecting. A screen bed about 18 inches to 22 inches square is a common size for collectors.

Tools and materials needed:
- Screw driver (An electric screw gun will reduce assembly time to minutes.)
- Hammer

- Wooden frame sides (4) — 1 inch x 3 inches x any length
Interior or exterior corner braces (4)
- Wood screws
- Wood staples (1/2 to 3/4 inch)
- Hardware cloth (Use 1/4 to 1/8 inch mesh for the screen. Most hardware stores carry a selection — 1/8 inch mesh is more difficult to locate, but worth the extra effort.)

Assembly:
Screw the frame together rather than nail it. The screws will hold the wood firmly in place and can be tightened if needed later. Next, screw the corner braces onto the frame to give it extra strength. Either interior (with an extra cross beam in the corner) or exterior braces work fine. Cut the hardware cloth to cover the bottom and make sure that it overlaps the wooden frame. Use wood staples (horseshoe nails) to secure the screen to the wood. Trim any mesh that sticks out from the edge of the frame. If the mesh edges are sharp, you can nail thin strips of wood across it or cover it with several layers of duct tape. The duct tape will need replacing periodically.

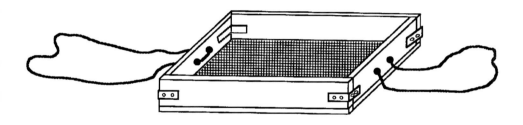

MINERAL AND EARTH SCIENCE CLUBS

If you are not familiar with the area you are traveling, the following selected organizations may be helpful for planning your trip. Earth science club meetings are the best source of local collecting information. Museums and geologic attractions often have exhibits containing local specimens. State and tourist agencies supply travel information.

PENNSYLVANIA

Beaver County Rock and Mineral Society
86 Academy Drive
Aliquippa, PA 15001

Berks Mineralogical Society
c/o 3417 River Road
Reading, PA 19605

Blair Rock & Mineral Club
RR 4, Box 187
Hollidaysburg, PA 16648

Bucks County Earth Science Society
c/o Churchville Nature Center
501 Churchville Lane
Churchville, PA 18966

Che-Hanna Rock and Mineral Club
P. O. Box 22
Sayre, PA 18840

Central Pennsylvania Rock & Mineral Club
2408 Swatara Street
Harrisburg, PA 17104

Delaware Valley Lapidary and Mineral Society
c/o 726 Sheffield Drive
Springfield, PA 19064

Delaware Valley Paleontological Society
P. O. Box 686
Plymouth Meeting, PA 19462

Franklin County Rock & Mineral Club
P. O. Box 1004
Chambersburg, PA 17201

Gem City Rock and Mineral Society, Inc.
c/o 427 Colleen Drive
Erie, PA 16505

Johnson Gem & Mineral Club
721 Casebeer Church Road
Somerset, PA 15501

Keystone West Gem & Mineral Society
508A Perry Highway
Harmony, PA 16037

Kishi Area Gem and Lapidary Club
RD #2
P.O. Box 132
Saltsburg, PA 15681

Kit-Han-Ne Rock and Gem Club
c/o Betty Milliron
200 Pine Hill Road
Kittanning, PA 16201

Mineral and Lapidary Society of Pittsburgh, Inc
c/o 409 E. Carter Drive
North Versailles, PA 15137

Mineralogical Society of Northeastern Pennsylvania
c/o 291 South Main Street
Pittston, PA 18640

Mineralogical Society of Pennsylvania
c/o 55 Hertzog School Road
Mertztown, PA 19539-9220

Monongahela Rockhounds
618 Nordean Drive
West Mifflin, PA 15122

Moraine Rockbusters, Inc.
c/o 4642 Hampton Valley Drive
Allison Park, PA 15101

New Castle Gem and Mineral Society
c/o 5086 Virginia Road
Hermitage, PA 16148

Nittany Mineralogical Society
Penn State University
122 Steidle Building
University Park, PA 16802

Pennsylvania Earth Sciences Association, Inc.
c/o 7582 Quarry Road
Alburtis, PA 18011

Philadelphia Mineralogical Society
c/o P. O. Box 40
Holicong, PA 18928

Rock and Mineral Club of Lower Bucks County
c/o 820 Sycamore Avenue
Croydon, PA 19021

Tuscarora Lapidary Society
c/o L. Howard Freeman Skill Center
105 W. Jasper Street
Media, PA 19063

York Rock and Mineral Club
c/o Dale Singer, Secretary
217 Hellam Street
Wrightsville, PA 17368

West Penn Micromineral Society
c/o 1221 Philippi Drive
Bethel Park, PA 15102

NEW JERSEY

Bergen County Mineralogy and Paleontology Society
c/o Eileen Jamieson, Editor
43 Cooper Street
Bergenfield, NJ 07621

Cape Atlantic Rockhounds
933 W. White Horse Pike
Egg Harbor, NJ 08215

Clifton Mineral & Lapidary Society
c/o Edward Murphy
337 Crystal Drive
Bricktown, NJ 08723

Delaware Valley Earth Science Society
c/o Gary Weinstein
1045 N. Maple Avenue
Maple Shade, NJ 08052

Franklin-Ogdensburg Mineralogical Society
P. O. Box 146
Franklin, NJ 07416-0146

Mineralogical and Lapidary Society of the Raritan Valley
c/o 106 Leghorn Avenue
Bridgewater, NJ 08807

Monmouth Mineral & Gem Club
P. O. Drawer J
Manasquan, NJ 08736-0640

Morris Museum Mineralogical Society
37 Rosedale Avenue
Madison, NJ 07940

Newark Mineralogical Society
54 Newman Avenue
Verona, NJ 07044

New Jersey Lapidary Society, Inc.
c/o 177 Broadway
Clark, NJ 07066

New Jersey Mineralogical Society
c/o 1240 S. 10th Street
South Plainfield, NJ 07080

New Jersey Paleontological Society
776 Asbury Street
New Milford, NJ 07646

North Jersey Mineralogical Society, Inc.
18-04 Hillery Street
Fair Lawn, NJ 07410-5207

The Trailside Mineral Club
160 Mountain Avenue
Warren, NJ 07060

Tri-County Mineral & Lapidary Society
337 Crystal Drive
Bricktown, NJ 08723

*Some collecting locations require membership in a club belonging to the Eastern Federation of Mineralogical Clubs and Lapidary Societies. Not all clubs listed are members of the Eastern Federation.

MUSEUMS

The following museums contain exhibits that are of interest to the rock and mineral collector. Many contain fine collections of rocks and minerals that are native to the state and region in which they are located.

PENNSYLVANIA

Academy of Natural Sciences
1900 Benjamin Franklin Parkway
Philadelphia, Pennsylvania 19103-1195
(215) 299-1000

Carnegie Institute Museum of Natural History
4400 Forbes Avenue
Pittsburgh, Pennsylvania 15213
(412) 622-3131

Delaware County Institute of Science
11 Veterans Square
Media, PA 19063
(610) 566-5126

Drake Well Museum
R.D. #3 Box 7
Titusville, PA 16354
(814) 827-2797

Earth and Mineral Science Museum
Pennsylvania State University
122 Steidle Building
University Park
State College, PA 16802
(814) 865-6427

Lycoming County Historical Museum
858 West Forth Street
Williamsport, PA 17701
(570) 326-3326

Museum of Anthracite Mining
17th and Pine Streets
Ashland, PA 17921
(570) 875-4708

Rennie Geology Museum
Department of Geology
Dickenson College
P. O. Box 1773
Carlisle, PA 17013-2896
(717) 245-1448

State Museum of Pennsylvania
P. O. Box 1026
Third and North Streets
Harrisburg, PA 17108-1026
(717) 787-4978

Tioga Point Museum
P. O. Box 143
724 South Main Street
Athens, PA 18810
(570) 888-7225

Tour-Ed Mine and Museum
R.D. 2
Tarentum, PA 15084
(412) 224-4720

Wagner Free Institute of Science
17th Street and Montgomery Avenue
Philadelphia, PA 19121
(215) 763-6529

NEW JERSEY

Ehrengart Museum
22 Woodport Road
Sparta, NJ 07871
(201) 729-3101
(Call before visit)

Franklin Mineral Museum
Evans Street
P. O. Box 54
Hamburg, New Jersey 07419
(973) 827-3481

Meadowlands Museum
91 Crane Avenue
Rutherford, NJ 07070
(201)935-1175

Morris Museum
6 Normandy Heights Road
Morristown, NJ 07960
(973) 538-0454

New Jersey State Museum
205 West State Street
P. O. Box 530
Trenton, NJ 08625-0530
(609) 292-6464

Paterson Museum
2 Market Street
Paterson, New Jersey 07501
(973) 881-3874

Rutgers University Geology Museum
Geology Hall
Rutgers University
New Brunswick, New Jersey 08903
(732) 932-7243

Sterling Hill Mining Museum
30 Plant Street
Ogdensburg, New Jersey 07439
(973) 209-7212

Appendix STATE GEOLOGIC SURVEYS

Pennsylvania Bureau of Topographic and Geological Survey
Department of Environmental Resources
P.O. Box 8453
Harrisburg, PA 17105-8453
(717) 787-2169

New Jersey Geological Survey
Division of Water Resources
P.O. Box 427
Trenton, NJ 08625
(609) 292-1185

STATE PARK INFORMATION _____

PENNSYLVANIA

Pennsylvania Bureau of State Parks
P. O. Box 8551
Harrisburg, PA 17105-8551
(800) 637-2757

State Parks Region 1 Office (North Central)
R.R. 4, Box 212
Emporium, PA 15834-9799
(814) 486-3365

State Parks Region 2 Office (Western)
P. O. Box 387
Prospect, PA 16052-0387
(724) 865-2131

State Parks Region 3 Office (South Central)
435 State Park Road
Schellsburg, PA 15559-9336
(814) 733-2202

State Parks Region 4 Office (Eastern)
2808 Three Mile Run Road
Perkasie, PA 18944-2065
(215) 453-5000

NEW JERSEY

New Jersey Division of Parks and Forestry
Attn: Public Information
P. O. Box 404
Trenton, NJ 08625
(800) 843-6420 (in NJ)
(609) 292-2797

TOURIST INFORMATION AGENCIES ——

PENNSYLVANIA

Bedford County Tourist Promotion Agency
141 S. Juliana Street
Bedford, PA 15522
(800) 765-3331
(814) 623-1771

Convention & Visitors Bureau of Blair County
Logan Valley Mall
Route 220 & Good Lane
Altoona, PA 16602
(800) 84-ALTOONA
(814) 943-4183

Bucks County Tourist Commission, Inc.
152 Swamp Road
Doylestown, PA 18901-2451
(800) 836-BUCKS

Cambria County Tourist Promotion Agency
111 Market Street
Johnstown, PA 15901-1608
(800) 237-8590
(814) 536-7993

Cameron County Tourist Promotion Agency
P. O. Box 118
Driftwood, PA 15832
(814) 546-2665

Centre County Lion Country Convention & Visitors Bureau
1402 South Atherton Street
State College, PA 16801
(800) 358-5466

Clinton County Tourist Promotion Agency, Inc.
Courthouse Annex
151 Susquehanna Avenue
Lock Haven, PA 17745
(570) 893-4037

Columbia-Montour Tourist Promotion Agency, Inc.
121 Papermill Road
Bloomsburg, PA 17815
(800) 847-4810
(570) 784-8279

Crawford County Tourist Association
926 Park Avenue
Meadville, PA 16335
(800) 332-2338

Cumberland Valley Visitors' Council
1235 Lincoln Way East
Chambersburg, PA 17201
(717) 261-1200

Delaware County Convention and Visitors Bureau
200 East State Street, Suite 100
Media, PA 19063
(800) 343-3983
(610) 565-3679

Elk County Tourist Promotion Agency
P. O. Box 35
Ridgeway, PA 15853
(814) 772-5502

Endless Mountains Visitors Bureau
R.R. 6, Box 132A
Tunkhannock, PA 18657
(570) 836-5431
(800) 769-8999

Erie Area Tourist and Convention Bureau
1006 State Street
Erie, PA 16501-1862
(814) 454-7191

Forest County Tourist Promotion Agency
P. O. Box 608
Tionesta, PA 16353
(800) 610-6611

Fulton County Tourist Promotion Agency
P. O. Box 141
McConnellsburg, PA 17233
(717) 485-4064

Gettysburg Travel Council
35 Carlisle Street
Gettysburg, PA 17325
(717) 334-6274

Harrisburg-Hershey-Carlisle Tourism and Convention Bureau
114 Walnut Street
Harrisburg, PA 17108-0969
(717) 231-7780
(800) 995-0969

Laurel Highlands, Inc.
120 E. Main Street
Ligonier, PA 15658
(800) 925-7669

Lawrence County Tourist Promotion Agency
138 West Washington Street
New Castle, PA 16101
(724) 654-5593

Lebanon Valley Tourist & Visitors Bureau
625 Quentin Road, Suite 4
Lebanon, PA 17042
(717) 272-8555

Lehigh Valley Convention and Visitors Bureau
P. O. Box 20785
Lehigh Valley, PA 18002-0785
(610) 882-9200

Lycoming County Tourist Promotion Agency
454 Pine Street
Williamsport, PA 17701
(800) 358-9900

Magic Forests of West Central Pennsylvania Tourism & Travel
    Bureau
Jefferson County Service Office
R.R. #5, Box 47
Brookville, PA 15825
(800) 348-9393

Mercer County Tourist Agency
One West State Street
Sharon, PA 16146
(800) 637-2370

Pennsylvania Dutch Convention & Visitors Bureau
501 Greenfield Road
Lancaster, PA 17601
(717) 299-8901

Pennsylvania's Northeast Territory Visitors Bureau
Airport Aviation Center
201 Hangar Road, Suite 203
Avoca, PA 18641
(800) 245-7711
(570) 457-1320

Perry County Tourist and Recreation Bureau
Courthouse
P. O. Box 447
New Bloomfield, PA 17068
(717) 582-2131

Philadelphia Convention and Visitors Center
16th Street & JFK Boulevard
Philadelphia, PA 19102
(215) 636-1666

Greater Pittsburgh Convention and Visitors Bureau
Four Gateway Center, Suite 514
Pittsburgh, PA 15222
(800) 366-0093

Potter County Recreation, Inc.
P. O. Box 245
Coudersport, PA 16915-0245
(814) 435-2290

Raystown Visitors Bureau
241 Mifflin Street
Huntingdon, PA 16652
(800) 269-4684
(814) 658-0060

Reading & Berks County Visitors Bureau
VF Outlet Village Complex
P. O. Box 6677
Reading, PA 19610
(610) 375-4085

Schuylkill County Visitors Bureau
91 S. Progress Avenue
Pottsville, PA 17901
(800) 765-7282
(570) 622-7700

Susquehanna Valley Visitors Bureau
P. O. Box 268
Lewisburg, PA 17837
(800) 458-4748

Travel Northern Alleghenies
P. O. Box 804
Warren, PA 16365
(800) 624-7802
(814) 726-1222

Valley Forge Convention and Visitors Bureau
600 West Germantown Pike
Plymouth Meeting, PA 19462
(800) 345-8112

Venango County Area Tourist Promotion Agency
Box 28
Franklin, PA 16323
(800) 776-4526

Wellsboro Area Chamber of Commerce
P. O. Box 733
Wellsboro, PA 16901
(570) 724-1926

York County Convention and Visitors Bureau
1 Market Way East
York, PA 17401
(800)673-2429

NEW JERSEY

In New Jersey, contact the Division of Travel and Tourism for information on local chambers of commerce, visitors bureaus, travel councils and attractions.

New Jersey Division of Travel and Tourism
20 W. State Street
P.O. Box 826
Trenton, NJ 08625-0826
(800) JERSEY-7

Coral Caverns
Route 31
Mann's Choice, PA 15550
(814) 623-6882

Crystal Cave Co., Inc.
R. D. #3, Box 416
Kutztown, PA 19530
(610) 683-6765

Indian Caverns
Spruce Creek, PA 16683
(814) 632-7578

Indian Echo Caverns
P. O. Box 188
368 Middletown Road
Hummelstown, PA 17036
(717) 566-8131

Laurel Caverns
R. D. #1, Box 10
Farmington, PA 15437
(724) 438-3003

Lincoln Caverns
R. R. #1, Box 280
Huntingdon, PA 16652
(814) 643-0268

Lost River Caverns
P. O. Box M
Hellertown, PA 18055
(610) 838-8767

Penn's Cave
R. D. #2, Box 165A
Route 129 East
Centre Hall, PA 16828
(814) 364-1664

Woodward Cave
P. O. Box 175
(Center Co., Route 45)
Woodward, PA 16882
(814) 349-9800

OTHER ATTRACTIONS

Batsto Village
c/o Wharton State Forest
RD #9
Hammonton, NJ 08037

Cornwall Iron Furnace
P.O. Box 251
Cornwall, PA 17016
(717) 272-9711

Fort Roberdeau
RD #3, Box 391
Altoona, PA 16601
(814) 946-0048

Lackawanna Coal Mine
McDade Park
Scanton, PA 18504
(800) 238-7245

Pioneer Tunnel Coal Mine
19th & Oak Streets
Ashland, PA 17921
(717) 875-3850

Strawberry Hill Nature Center and Preserve
1537 Mount Hope Road
Fairfield, PA 17320
(717) 642-5840

MINERAL LOCATOR INDEX

MINERAL LOCATOR INDEX

GLOSSARY

Aggregate - A grouping or cluster of crystals or mineral grains.

Ammonoid - An extinct group of cephalopods similar in appearance to the modern nautilus.

Amphibole - A family of minerals containing silicates of magnesium, iron and calcium such as actinolite, tremolite and hornblende. Amphiboles are frequently associated with metamorphic and igneous rocks.

Barite - A mineral, barium sulfate, with orthorhombic crystals and a high specific gravity. Barite is the ore for barium, which has many industrial uses.

Basalt - The most common extrusive igneous rock or lava, basalt is primarily composed of pyroxene and feldspar. Highly fluid basalt that quickly covers a large area is referred to as flood basalt.

Bog Iron - A poor-quality iron ore found as deposits of hydrous iron oxides, known as goethite or limonite, at the bottom of bogs or swamps.

Borrow Pit - A small excavation often found near roadways or other construction projects. Material from the pit was "borrowed" as fill for the construction.

Brachiopod - A marine invertebrate from the phylum *Brachiopoda*, it is formed of two shells of unequal size that are bilaterally symmetrical. Frequently found as fossils, brachiopods survive to the present.

Carbonate - A group of minerals which on a chemical level are inorganic salts of carbonic acid. Most frequently encountered are the common carbonates calcite or dolomite or their related rocks limestone and dolomite. Mineral collectors may be familiar with some of the seventy or so carbonate minerals including aragonite, siderite, strontianite, azurite and malachite.

Chert - Cryptocrystalline sedimentary rock similar to flint. White, black, gray or banded chert is often found as nodules within limestone and dolomite layers.

Chromite - Primary ore of chromium found as small, black octahedral crystals.

Coelenterates - A diverse group of soft-bodied sea animals frequently found as fossils (also known as cnidarians) including sea anemones and jellyfish.

Concretions - Lumps or nodules formed within sedimentary layers often composed from concentrations of minerals. Concretions sometimes form around fossils or interesting minerals.

Cretaceous Period - Final period of geologic time within the Mesozoic Era 135-65 million years ago. Marine sediment containing many of New Jersey's most famous fossils were deposited at this time.

Crinoid - A family of echinoderms surviving to the present (commonly known as "sea lily"), but often found as fossils. The stem which anchored the "flower" to the sea bottom is most often recovered.

Dendrite - Branch-like or moss-like pattern of minerals often mistaken for fossils.

Devonian - A geologic time period of the Paleozoic era approximately 345-395 million years ago.

Diabase - An intrusive igneous rock primarily containing pyroxene and feldspar.

Dolomite - Both a common carbonate rock and a mineral, dolomite forms when magnesium replaces the calcium in limestone.

Double-terminated - Refers to a mineral crystal, such as quartz, which has a termination or point on each end.

Fluorite - A halide group mineral frequently purple, but also found as green, yellow or blue in color.

Franklinite - A zinc and iron-manganese ore found chiefly in northern New Jersey near Franklin. The black metallic octahedral crystals are associated with zincite and willemite in calcite.

Gastropods - A mollusk, snail or slug, mostly with a single coiled shell. Fossil gastropods are important index fossils of the Tertiary geological time period.

Gemmy - Gem-like or having gem-like qualities; a subjective rather than scientific term.

Glauberite - A combination of salts found in dry regions. The prismatic crystals sometimes leave behind their characteristic shapes as pseudomorphs in surrounding minerals such as quartz.

Goethite - A red, brown or yellow iron mineral commonly encountered as limonite (see Bog Iron).

Hornblende - A common member of the amphibole group typically black to dark green and found in metamorphic and igneous rocks.

Hornfels - A finely grained metamorphic rock metamorphosed by heat in the contact region near a subterranean igneous intrusion.

Igneous Rock - Rock formed from molten magma either above the surface (extrusive or volcanic) or within the crust (intrusive or plutonic).

Inclusion - Mineral crystals enclosed within a larger host mineral specimen. Inclusions may also be gas bubbles or liquid-filled cavities.

Kyanite - A typically blue to gray aluminum-rich mineral found in high pressure metamorphic rock.

Limonite - The most common form of goethite (see goethite).

Lithification - The process of conversion from sediments to rock. The process may be achieved by compaction, cementation, crystallization and even desiccation.

Magothy Formation - Cretaceous geologic formation exposed at several points in New Jersey and Delaware.

Mahantango Formation - A middle Devonian geological formation exposed in Pennsylvania about 387 million years old.

Marcasite - A sulfide mineral closely related to pyrite.

Matrix - The surrounding material in which a mineral or fossil specimen is contained.

Metamorphic Rock - Any rock that has been changed by heat and/or pressure.

Mineral Blade - Blade-like and sometimes radiating portions of mineral crystals.

Outcrop - Rock exposed at the surface.

Pegmatite - Coarse-grained igneous rock such as granite that typically cooled slowly beneath the Earth's surface.

Pelecypods - Aquatic mollusks such as clams, mussels, oysters, or scallops. Frequently found as fossils, they are useful as indices in dating formations.

Pennsylvanian Period - North American name used for the Upper Carboniferous period 325-280 million years ago. Named for the abundant Upper Carboniferous period rock and fossil exposed by coal mining in Pennsylvania.

Permian Period - Geologic period 280-225 million years ago. The final folding of the Appalachian Mountains in Pennsylvania occurred during the Permian.

Phosphorescence - Visible light that radiates after the source of energy is removed. Some fluorescent minerals of northern New Jersey continue to glow for a while after an UV light is turned off.

Phyllite - A silvery metamorphic rock derived from sedimentary rock.

Pleistocene Epoch - A relatively recent geologic epoch ending just 10,000 years ago and part of the Cenozoic period. The Pleistocene is generally thought of as "ice age" time with many of the great mammals such as the mastodon, woolly mammoth and saber-tooth cat.

Pre-Cambrian Period - The oldest and largest geologic period extending from 570 million years ago to 4.6 billion years ago. The ancient Baltimore Gneiss metamorphic rock in the Philadelphia area formed in this time.

Pseudomorph - A mineral sometimes replaces another mineral taking the physical shape of the original, but not its internal crystal structure. Likewise, a mineral like quartz may coat another less durable mineral like glauberite. When the original mineral dissolves, a relic mineral shape or skeletal pseudomorph may remain.

Rhombic - More properly, the orthorhombic crystal system, for which it is a synonym.

Scarp - A cliff caused by erosion or geologic faulting.

Schist - A metamorphic rock defined by the parallel arrangement of its minerals rather than the composition. Schist is often rich with mica, hornblende and even kyanite.

Seam - A visible line of rock or mineral passing through a larger mass of rock such as a seam of quartz in a limestone quarry wall.

Sedimentary Rock - Rock formed from the consolidation of sediments (see Lithification).

Serpentine - A low grade and often fibrous metamorphic rock often having lapidary potential and a variety of local names such as "Eastonite."

Shale - A fine grain sedimentary rock composed of compacted silt, clay or sand frequently containing fossil remains.

Siderite - An iron carbonate mineral.

Silting - The accumulation of fine sedimentary particles that over geologic time may form siltstone.

Silurian Period - Geologic time period 435-395 million years ago. Much of Pennsylvania's metamorphic slate belt formed from sedimentary shale in the Silurian.

Single-terminated - A crystal such as quartz with a single point or termination.

Sphalerite - A sulfide mineral found in variety of colors such as red, yellow, brown or black. Sphalerite is often associated with pegmatites or hydrothermal minerals such as galena and chalcopyrite.

Strontianite - A white carbonate, usually a radiating fibrous mass, found in association with barite, celestite, and calcite. In Pennsylvania it occurs in low-temperature hydrothermal veins in limestone.

Sulfide - A group of minerals that have a metal combined with sulfur such as galena, marcasite, chalcopyrite and pyrite.

Talus Slope - A slope of rough debris at the foot of a cliff caused by weathering or other action.

Tectonic Plate - Enormous slowly moving plates that comprise the Earth's crust. Eight major plates and many smaller plates shift across the mantle causing most of the large scale geologic changes on the Earth.

Triassic Period - First geologic period of the Mesozoic Era 225–195 million years ago. Footprints of early Triassic dinosaurs are found in both Pennsylvania and New Jersey.

Vug - A cavity within a rock often filled or partially filled with crystallized minerals such as zeolites.

Willemite - Zinc silicate mineral. Willemite from zinc mines in Northern New Jersey are famous for their bright-green glow under UV light.

Zeolite - A hydrated group of minerals including natrolite, stilbite, and heulandite often found in cavities in basalt and related hydrothermal areas. The flood basalts of New Jersey produce some of the finest collector specimens of zeolites in the world.

Zircon - A silicate mineral often found in igneous and metamorphic rocks. Zircon is the ore for zirconium.

OTHER TITLES FOR ROCKHOUNDS

The Gem Trails Series is the definitive line of rockhound guidebooks to the best collecting sites for gems, minerals and fossils throughout each state. Detailed text, road maps, directions, B/W photos lead the way and vivid color photos of specimens showcase future finds. From micro-mount and gem quality mineral specimens to fossil pieces containing life-like forms that are millions of years old, there is something of interest to both the novice and experienced collector.

GEM TRAILS OF ARIZONA, *Mitchell.*
184 pgs., ISBN 0-935182-82-9, $9.95

GEM TRAILS OF COLORADO, *Mitchell.*
144 pgs., ISBN 0-935182-91-8, $9.95

GEM TRAILS OF NEVADA, *Mitchell.*
119 pgs., ISBN 0-935182-53-5, $6.95

GEM TRAILS OF NEW MEXICO, *Mitchell.*
160 pgs., ISBN 1-889786-12-8, $10.95

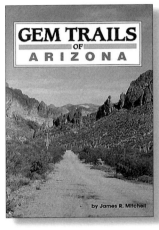

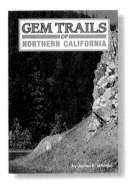

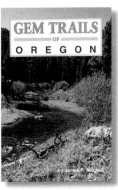

GEM TRAILS OF NORTHERN CALIFORNIA, *Mitchell.*
160 pgs., ISBN 0-935182-67-5, $9.95

GEM TRAILS OF OREGON, *Mitchell.*
192 pgs., ISBN 0-935182-99-3, $10.95

GEM TRAILS OF SOUTHERN CALIFORNIA, *Mitchell.*
184 pgs., ISBN 0-935182-83-7, $8.95

GEM TRAILS OF TEXAS, *Mitchell.*
96 pgs., ISBN 0-935182-34-9, $7.95

GEM TRAILS OF UTAH, *Mitchell.*
168 pgs., ISBN 0-935182-87-X, $9.95

DESERT GEM TRAILS, *Strong.*
80 pgs., ISBN 0-910652-15-5, $5.00

MIDWEST GEM, FOSSIL AND MINERAL TRAILS: Great Lakes States, *Zeitner.* This newly revised edition describes where and what to collect in Minnesota, Wisconsin, Indiana, Illinois, Michigan and Ohio. Learn how to hunt on your own, what collectibles can be found and how to preserve your specimens.
128 pgs., ISBN 1-889786-06-3, $10.95

MIDWEST GEM, FOSSIL & MINERAL TRAILS: Prairie States, *Zeitner.* First published in 1955, this updated edition describes where and what to collect in Kansas, Nebraska, Missouri, North Dakota, South Dakota, and Iowa, how to hunt on your own and where to get more information and additional help in each state.
128 pgs., ISBN 0-935182-94-2, $10.95

ROCKHOUND'S HANDBOOK, *Mitchell.* Learn about rock and mineral formation, tools, identification, finding minerals in the field, legal aspects preparation and preservation, cutting and polishing, and making jewelry from your finds. Numerous illustrations and B/W photos. Color photos highlight over 50 of the most commonly encountered minerals.
194 pgs., ISBN 0-935182-90-X, $12.95

ROCKHOUNDING EASTERN NEW YORK & NEARBY NEW ENGLAND, *Zabriskie.* Mineral and fossil collecting sites located with maps, directions and the specimens found at each location.
60 pgs., $8.95

AVAILABLE AT YOUR LOCAL BOOKSTORE, ROCKSHOP OR OUTDOOR STORE.

NOTES